Me? I'm From Iowa

Brothers Francis & Eugene Francois

ME? I'M FROM IOWA

Memoirs of an Iowa Farm Boy Who Went to Washington

FRANCIS B. FRANCOIS

FRANCOIS PRESS
260 Victoria Street E4, Costa Mesa, CA 92627

1 3 5 7 9 10 8 6 4 2

Library of Congress Cataloging-in-Publication Data
Francois, Francis B., 1934-
Me? I'm from Iowa: Memoirs of an Iowa farm boy who
went to Washington / Francis B. Francois
ISBN: 978-1-105-25880-0
p. cm.
1. Francois, Francis B., 1936– 2. Iowa – United States -
Biography. I. Title

Cover and Interior design by Michael D. Francois
Distributed by Lulu

Dedicated to my children and grandchildren.
-- FBF

Also by Francis B. Francois:

> *Two Guys From Barnum, Iowa And How They Helped*
> *Save Basketball: A History of U.S. Patent 4,534,556:*
> *Paul D. Estuland and Kenneth F. Estlund,*
> *Inventors.* (ISBN 978-0-615-18342-8)

Front Cover Photograph: Francis B. Francois, about 8 years old, on the Weiss farm.

PREFACE

These memoirs are about a boy who was born on an Iowa farm in January 1934 and his travels through life until now – me.

In my life I have had the chance to travel in all 50 States of the United States of America and in over 30 other nations, and to meet and talk with many, many people. In my careers and on my travels I have often been asked, "Where are you from?" My common answer has been, "Me? I'm from Iowa." To me this answer sums up much of who I am and what I have become. Thus, when I undertook the writing of these memoirs I chose *Me? I'm from Iowa* as the title.

Why write my memoirs? Mainly, to put on paper something about me and my family, to help answer some of the questions that our children, their children, and their children's children and our friends may have. What I have written here may also be of interest to others, both Iowans and people who have never set foot in the Hawkeye State.

In addition to telling about growing up in Iowa, I want to explore some of the Iowa impacts upon me and my life that helped evolve my way of thinking and acting through my life and careers. I hope that in addition to providing information, what I have written will entertain readers and give some enjoyment.

These memoirs do not provide detailed information about my ancestors. That information is contained in two other earlier volumes I wrote, *The Peter Francois and Anne Barbian Family*, and *The McDonough Family of Webster County, Iowa*. First editions of these two volumes were self-published in the early 1990's, and revised editions are now in preparation with the help of my son Michael.

This volume has been under development for many years. Some of the material was first drafted in 1984 when I turned 50, and text was often written while I was traveling and had a laptop computer with me. These memoirs are not all-inclusive but rather are selective in content, presenting things which have seemed important to me and which have stayed in my memory all these years. Since these things are remembered by me I can only conclude that they are a part of whatever I have become.

There have been many source documents used to prepare this volume, including census data, and information collected over the years from family members and the Fort Dodge Public Library. Of special value was a one-page summary of the McDonough family given to me by my Aunt, Alice McDonough. I have also received comments and valuable editing from members of the Francois and McDonough families, all of whom I thank.

The language and grammar used here sometimes draws on terms from our Iowa farming community and my Irish and German family background. One decision I had to make was how to refer to my parents, Rudolph John Francois and Irene Frances McDonough Francois. In some instances I use the common terms "father" and "mother" when referring to them, but I also use the terms "Pa" and "Ma" since this was our everyday way of talking, and occasionally "Dad" and "Mom." My mother called her mother "Ma," and we referred to her as "Grandma." Ma usually called Pa Rudy, as did many of our friends, and he called her Irene or ma. Tracing back to his German heritage, Pa was also often called "Dutch."

In my 77 years many wonderful things have happened to me, and I have had many blessings. The greatest of these blessings was meeting and marrying my wonderful wife, Eileen Mary Schmelzer, who went to heaven on October 22, 2003. We were married on February 6, 1960 at St. John Baptist de la Sales Catholic Church in Chillum, Maryland, and had five wonderful children, Joseph Francis, Marie Eileen, Michael David, Monica Irene, and Susan Rose, and as of this writing seven grandchildren:

Brendan, Conor and Alison (by Joe and his wife, Mary-Lynne Neal); Eileen, Elizabeth and Julia (by Marie and her husband, Juan Rodriguez); and Ash Declan (adopted by Monica and her husband, Anthony Marcel). Nothing in my life means more to me than these people, and these memoirs are dedicated to them. Indeed, without them and their support these memoirs could not have been written.

A special thank you to Michael and Susan. Susan edited the draft, and Michael handled the publication process, and both provided much advice.

FOREWORD

This book deals with that portion of North America where the United States of America exists. When Christopher Columbus arrived in America this land mass was in the hands of those we call Native Americans, who were spread broadly across the land and who were organized into over 500 tribes ranging from small to large. These Native Americans were here for thousands of years, and had organized themselves into societies that covered the North and South American continents. In the United States and Mexico we find the remains of civilizations that once flourished, and which left monuments behind. In time people from Europe and possibly China and/or Japan crossed the oceans and discovered the American continents.

We commonly say that Christopher Columbus discovered America, although there is evidence that other cultures may have preceded him by many years. In any case Columbus' first voyage was acclaimed and set off an explosion, with nearly endless shiploads of people from other lands coming here and building communities. These settlers were mostly Europeans, and they set about settling the land and establishing governments based on what they had in their homelands with changes that they thought would serve them well. As time went on a new kind of nation emerged in the late 1700s, the United States of America.

The United States began on the eastern seaboard, except for Spanish people who settled in the southwest and southeast. After the Revolutionary War and the establishment of the first states, Americans began to move west over the mountains to settle them and build new communities. The nation adopted Manifest Destiny as its theme, meaning the nation should spread from ocean to ocean. The Native Americans often opposed this expansion, and fighting sometimes resulted. Over the years a host of treaties were entered into between the new settlers and the Native Americans, many of which were broken over time by the settlers when they decided to claim reserved land and resources for themselves.

The people from Europe and elsewhere who came to America traveled by ship from a port in the Old Country, to a port established here. Some American ports were right on the ocean, and others were further inland where they could be reached by sailing up a river or bay. Once off the ship and on dry land, walking or riding a horse, donkey or mule were the universal means of moving across America. Some people also went by water and used the Mississippi River, the Ohio River, and the Great Lakes to move about. In the early 1800s the Erie Canal and some other waterways were built that offered faster transportation. The canals were followed by the railroads in the mid 1800s, in much of the developing nation. Some primitive roads were built, and over time stagecoach transportation was available in some areas.

This book concentrates on my German and Irish ancestors who came to the United States from their home countries in the mid 1800s, and who went to the Midwest to settle, the Germans in Wisconsin, and the Irish in Iowa. I explain how my family settled in America, tell something about their lives, and then report on my life and activities.

1

A Little About Iowa and Fort Dodge

Some Iowa History

To the Native Americans who resided on its rolling hills, flat plains and along its rivers, what became the State of Iowa was the "beautiful land." According to legend, the term for "beautiful land" in the language of some of the tribes of Native Americans was "Iowa," which is how the area got its name. Its nickname is "The Hawkeye State."

Iowa is located in the middle of what is now the continental United States, between the Mississippi River on the east and the Missouri and Big Sioux Rivers on the west, south of the State of Minnesota and north of the State of Missouri. The western edge of Iowa faces South Dakota and Nebraska, and the eastern border faces Wisconsin and Illinois. Iowa was acquired by the United States in 1803, when President Thomas Jefferson moved ahead with the Louisiana Purchase from France.

The first Europeans to visit Iowa are believed to have been French fur traders and missionaries, who came in the 1700s by canoe to trade with the Native American tribes along the rivers and convert them to Catholicism. The two most prominent tribes in Iowa were the Sac and Fox, currently named the Mesquakie Indians. About 17 tribes lived in the State at various times.

Iowa was home for many of these Native Americans before the Europeans came and undertook efforts to remove them from land that settlers might want. In the early days of the European expansion over America there were a number of wars fought between the settlers and the Indian tribes, such as the French and Indian War in Colonial times and several others in the east. These military efforts continued in both the East and the West until almost the start of the 20th Century – indeed, the Seminole tribe in Florida never did surrender to the United States.

The Black Hawk War

As part of its policy of developing the geography of the United States, in the early 1800s it was proposed that the Native Americans be moved beyond the Mississippi River, and that Europeans settle east of that river. As a result, settlers began to move into Ohio, Indiana, Illinois, and Wisconsin, with the support of the U.S. Army where needed. Along the Mississippi River there was a band of Native Americans who were based in Iowa, but who also liked to live and camp east of the River in Wisconsin and Illinois. The U.S. Army told their chief, Black Hawk, that they could not live east of the Mississippi River, but needed to move to Iowa or further west. Black Hawk and his elders objected to doing this, and the U.S. Army proceeded to undertake forcibly moving them back into Iowa. This produced what became known as the Black Hawk War of 1832.

After several skirmishes in which there were deaths on both sides, the Native Americans accepted defeat and crossed back into Iowa. One humorous story from that war was that Abraham Lincoln was an officer, and he himself was short on training. He needed to have the troops move through a gate in the fence but could not recall the command, so he dismissed the troops, and told them to reform on the other side of he fence.

The war opened Iowa, Illinois and Wisconsin for settlement. Following the war, the Native Americans were forced to cede their property rights in Iowa to the United States as an indemnity for the war, at a price of about 11 cents per acre. The Native Americans were asked to move further west by June 1, 1833. Other tribes also had their interests in Iowa purchased by the Federal government, and by 1845 all of the tribes had agreed to move west of Iowa.

In 1833, following the end of the war, the flow of new people into what became Iowa began in earnest as settlers from Illinois, Indiana and other eastern states moved across the Mississippi River onto the new lands. These new Iowans included both new immigrants, and persons from earlier times who had settled on farms in the east but wanted to move to Iowa. How did they get to Iowa? There were no superhighways to travel, and the railroads had just started planning for building across the Mississippi River into Iowa. Coming from the east, most people would take the railroads as far west as possible, and then travel by horse or oxen and wagon, paying to cross the river. Two alternatives included taking the Ohio River down to the Mississippi and then barging up the Mississippi River, or coming down to Iowa from the Illinois River. Once in Iowa, there were several hundred miles to go to get deeply into the State where the best available farms were.

By 1855 regular stagecoach service was provided within Iowa, at first on a weekly basis and later bi-weekly. According to the booklet "Webster's Prairies" published by the Webster County Bicentennial Commission in 1976, "the most important stage coach line was the North Western Stage Company out of Iowa City, which provided service to Dubuque, Sioux City and Des Moines."

"Travel on the stage was neither comfortable nor cheap. The roads were rough and if the stage became mired in the mud the passenger was expected to lend a strong back to pushing it out. The fare from Dubuque to Fort Dodge was a $20 gold piece. Even after the railroads arrived in 1869, smaller stage companies continued to operate for several years, north to Algona and the surrounding area."

By 1846 Iowa was sufficiently established within its present boundaries that the Congress of the United States admitted it to the Union as the 29th State. The original capitol was Iowa City, which is located in the southeast corner of the State, but as the years went by a new, more centrally located capitol was established in Des Moines, along the Des Moines River that runs northwest across the State from its southeast Iowa juncture with the Mississippi River.

Getting Settled and Organizing the State

Those coming to Iowa had to choose a location to settle, and prepare for their new lives. Some had been farmers and knew how to proceed. Others had to learn as they went along. All had available to them lots of advice, from the railroads and others who saw profit from the settlements, and from immigrant organizations.

Generally, it was said that pioneers would need about $400 in U.S. money of the early 1800s to set themselves up on a farm of about 40 acres, "with a log house, a good yoke of oxen, a horse, a cow, 12 sheep, etc.... and farming utensils generally, with 30 week's provisions laid in until a small crop is raised for subsistence." This was not an easy undertaking, and called on all members of the family to work hard. For land, the settler looked for good cropland on a stream or with other water available, and with a good stand of trees from which to build a house and other buildings. The settlers needed to have shovels, axes and other tools to carry out their work.

One of the first things the new Iowans had to do was form a state government, and set up an overall governing system. The Iowa Constitution was modeled on those of other states. Locally, the Iowans chose to adopt the county government system. One of the first tasks that needed to be done was to survey the entire state, so that property could be identified and deeds and mortgages written. Private contractors surveyed most of Iowa during the years 1836 through 1859, using the fifth north-south prime meridian as the eastern boundary and an east-west base line through Little Rock, Arkansas for numbering from south to north.

The State was surveyed to divide it into 99 counties, sometimes using techniques that resulted in minor errors. For example, a common way to measure mileage was to drive across the land and count the number of wagon wheel revolutions until the distance wanted was reached and then staking a boundary. On flat, smooth ground this worked reasonably well, but if the covered ground was rough or wet, there were often errors in the reported mileage and the stake locations. The surveyors were charged with running a correction line ever six miles, but again these also could vary in accuracy.

The basic subdivision unit of the State was a one mile square section of land that contained 640 acres, usually divided into four 160 acre plats, eight 80 acre plats, or sixteen 40 acre plats. Because of the somewhat crude survey techniques used, some plots of land on the western edge of a section might be several acres smaller or larger than what was called for. To avoid later arguments, it was common for Iowa land deeds to avoid specifying acreage but rather to use a fraction of the section.

Each county was typically divided into 36 numbered townships, six townships in a tier and numbered from south to north. One section of land in each township was dedicated to education. Both counties and townships in

Iowa are usually named after a well-known person. For example, my home county is Webster County, named after Daniel Webster, and my farm is located in Jackson Township, named after President Jackson.

Counties came to the United States from Great Britain, and each has a county seat where legal contests are tried, judges hear criminal charges, and legal documents are recorded. The usual goal was to locate the county seat so that a resident could ride a horse to it, do business and then come home the same day.

Fort Dodge and Webster County

I was born and grew up in Webster County, located in northwest Iowa on the Des Moines River. The county seat is Fort Dodge, a city of about 25,000. It started out in 1850 as a fort for Federal troops stationed in Iowa to protect against Indian raids. Brevet Major Samuel Woods led the Federal troops charged with establishing the fort. He and his aides chose the site, and proceeded to build a stockade fort and some 20 buildings in time for the troops to move inside before the winter came. The surrounding area had good water available, timber, and there was stone nearby for building and coal for heating. It was contemplated that the fort might some day be a town, and the buildings were strung in a line that might be a future street.

The first name for the fort was Fort Clarke, but it was found there already was a fort by that name. In 1851 the fort's name was changed to Fort Dodge. In 1853 the army decided that the troops in the fort should move north into Minnesota to be nearer the Sioux Indians, and the army closed down Fort Dodge as a military location. William Williams, who had run the fort's store, purchased the fort, with its land and buildings. He in turn plotted out a town named Fort Dodge in March 1854, and as the years went by people came there to live.

Native American Attacks

As stated the Federal Government built Ft. Dodge to protect settlers in the area. Because there were no serious threats the Fort was closed in 1853, as noted. But a major incident occurred in the spring of 1857, in which a small band of Sioux Indians murdered a large family, except for a 14-year old girl, the only survivor. The Sioux band, headed by Chief Inkpaduta, also killed several other persons. The event is known as the Spirit Lake Massacre. Today the Lake and others near it in the northwest corner of Iowa are known as summer resorts.

The spring of 1857 was bitter cold in northwest Iowa, with lots of snow. It took many days for anyone to reach Ft. Dodge and Webster City, to report on the massacre. A number of men in each town volunteered to go, about 80 in all, providing their own food and supplies. They elected Major William Williams to head the expedition. One person who volunteered was Martin McDonough, a relative of mine, who was not allowed to go because of health problems.

The trip both ways was brutal, with the cold reaching 30 below. Some froze to death, and frozen limbs were common. Several of the rescuers died. No victims were alive except for Abbie Gardiner. The rescuers buried the dead victims, many of whom had been scalped.

The next year a similar attack occurred in Minnesota, but this was the last attack in Iowa.

For those interested in the Massacre, I urge you to read *Spirit Lake* by MacKinley Kantor. A Pulitzer Prize winner, Kantor was born in Webster City, Iowa.

Land Office Business

In the mid-1850s a Federal land office was located in Fort Dodge, which meant that anyone buying land in

Iowa's northwest corner had to come to Fort Dodge. This caused a rapid spurt in population. The years 1855 to 1857 saw the massive sale of federal lands, and fortunes were made and lost. The minimum bid on these lands was $1.25 per acre, and a few months later it sold for $8.00 to $12.00 per acre. It was estimated that about 1,000 people were in Fort Dodge at the end of 1857, and that between 20,000 and 25,000 acres of land were auctioned off each day at the height of the fever. Collapse in this market came in 1857 and as a result many left Fort Dodge for elsewhere. But most stayed, and among them were several persons from Ireland, including the man and woman who were to become the fraternal grandparents of my mother, Irene Frances McDonough.

The people who came to Iowa were mostly from Northern Europe. By 1850 the total population of Iowa had reached 192,214, and ten years later it was 674,913. By 1900 there were 2,231,853 Iowans, and in 2006 it was estimated that the population had reached 2,982,085. In 2004 it was estimated that the eight largest ancestry groups in Iowa are: German (35.7 %); Irish (13.5%); English (9.5%); American (6.6%); Norwegian (5.7%); Dutch (4.6%); Swedish (3.3%) and Danish (3.2%). The population of the State in the 2000 Federal census was predominantly white (96.14%) with 2.51% of the people being black, 0.63% American Indian, 1.48% Asian, and 0.08% Hawaiian or Pacific.

During the 1850s there was a dispute about which town should be the county seat, between the people in Fort Dodge, which is essentially in the center of Webster County, and the residents of another town called Homer located some 25 miles southeast of Fort Dodge. Fort Dodge won the contest, and in 1856 was made the seat of Webster County by the Iowa Legislature. The first court session was held in Fort Dodge that same year. Homer, having lost the argument, faded away over the years.

A most important issue for Iowa and all the prairie states was the locating of the new railroads businessmen were competing to build, and the leaders of Fort Dodge worked very hard on this issue. In 1856 locational studies for the Dubuque and Pacific Railroad were completed, and the route passed through Fort Dodge. Fort Dodge voted for $200,000 as a grant to the railroad company if construction began at once, and the Iowa Legislature voted a land grant to the Dubuque and Pacific Railroad. The 1857 panic slowed the construction, but the railroad was finally completed in 1869. The Fort Dodge railroad station boosted the importance of the fledgling county seat, as did the completion of a railroad link with Des Moines in the same year.

In the early 1900s the Fort Dodge, Des Moines and Southern Line was organized, and it built an interurban railroad that ran down Central Avenue in Fort Dodge and which connected the city with the State Capitol in Des Moines. I rode this line once, and it was a delightful ride through the Iowa farmland and some beautiful landscapes. When the line was built it joined a host of such interurban or light rail lines across the Midwest, which flourished for a few decades. Now all those lines are gone, the Fort Dodge, Des Moines and Southern Line ending its life after some 40 years. The automobile was more friendly and easier to use, and over the years replaced most passenger rail service.

In 1857 the first Catholic Church in Northwest Iowa , Corpus Christi, was built in Fort Dodge, responding to the large number of Irish and other Catholic settlers. A number of Irish came to Fort Dodge around 1855. According to a 1913 book, The History of Fort Dodge and Webster County Iowa, Webster County had a total population of 2,504 by 1860, which increased to 7,812 by 1869.

1856 Iowa Census

The Ft. Dodge Public Library has a microfilm copy of an 1856 Iowa census for Wahkonsa Township in Webster County, in which Ft. Dodge is located. Among the entries are the following:

> *Patrick McDonough, age 35, born in Ireland, farmer*
> *Mary McDonough, age 34, born in Ireland*

This Patrick McDonough is believed to be the brother of Terence McDonough, and would support an arrival date in Ft. Dodge of 1854 or 1855 for Patrick. In the Alice McDonough document, she states that Terence arrived in Ft. Dodge in 1854, which probably means that Patrick and Terence came together at that time. However, the author could find no mention of Terence McDonough in the 1856 Iowa census. This could be because he was located elsewhere on the day that the census taker recorded Patrick and Mary.

According to Alice McDonough, Terence McDonough came to Iowa from Ohio. Whether the same is true of Patrick McDonough is unknown. Thus far I have not been able to find further evidence of an Ohio residence for Terence.

As to how Patrick and Terence came to Ft. Dodge in the 1850's, they first left Ireland by ship and came to New York. They then started moving west, probably by railroad. Many Irish first went to the coalmines of Pennsylvania or to farms or other jobs in Ohio, or to jobs in the growing Chicago area. As noted, Alice McDonough mentioned that Terence came from Ohio. I was also told that some relatives lived in Pennsylvania for a while, around the coalmines. In time Patrick and Terence moved toward Iowa, crossed the Mississippi River, and then traveled to Fort Dodge.

A railroad from Illinois crossed the river and went to Walcott, Iowa in 1855, a town just west of Davenport located some 240 miles from Fort Dodge. Many people used barges to cross the Mississippi to reach Iowa, and then rented transportation to Fort Dodge. I do not know how my McDonough ancestors reached Fort Dodge.

Coming of the Railroads

Among the railroads that reached Fort Dodge was one that ran east and west from Chicago to Sioux City, known in my youth as the Illinois Central Railroad, with stations in Barnum and Ft. Dodge. According to the 1870 publication *Iowa: The Home for Immigrants*, what became the Illinois Central Railroad line from Chicago to Sioux City started out across the state of Iowa going west from Dubuque, Iowa, as the Dubuque and Sioux City Railroad, to as far as Iowa Falls. West of Iowa Falls the line was called the Iowa Falls and Sioux City Railroad, and it did not reach Fort Dodge until 1869.

The Illinois Central Railroad, it should be noted, no longer operates between Chicago and Sioux City. It abandoned this route several years ago, and the route is now operated by a regional railroad. In its prime, the Illinois Central Railroad operated both passenger and freight service on this line, including sleeping car service between Sioux City and Chicago. When I left Iowa in June 1956 to journey to Washington, D.C., the first leg of the trip was a sleeping car from Fort Dodge to Chicago, on the Illinois Central. In Chicago, I had to change train stations to catch a sleeper train headed for Washington, DC. The activity of transferring from one station to another in Chicago was then a major business in that city, with four major train stations. Today, the transfer business no longer exists, as Chicago now has only one station.

As time progressed the railroads came to Iowa, slowly building their way from east to west and north and south across the State. One of the major railroads was the Chicago and Northwestern, which reached Council Bluffs on the western edge of the State in 1867; it was later connected with the Union Pacific to complete the first coast- to- coast railroad. The Minneapolis and St. Louis Railroad connected Minneapolis with St. Louis via Des Moines, and the Rock Island Line ran northwest to Minneapolis and on to the west coast. By the late 1800's Iowa, like Ohio, Illinois and other Mid-west farm States, had an extensive railroad system that allowed many rural residents to go to their county seats and other towns to do business and shop.

The coming of the railroads was important to Iowa, one reason being that they provided construction and then railroad operating jobs to immigrants, especially the Irish, who were good manual labor workers. By the mid-1850s there were many Irish in Fort Dodge, including my great grandfather, Terence McDonough, and his brother, Patrick McDonough.

Barnum, Clare and Manson

The railroads wanted to haul people and freight, and to further this goal they would often establish towns about every 10 to 12 miles along their tracks where they would build a railroad station, sometimes named after officers of the railroad. Three such towns played an Important part in my family story; Barnum, located west of Fort Dodge on the Chicago-Sioux City line, called the Illinois Central Railroad when I was growing up; Manson, on the same railroad and located about 10 miles west of Barnum; and Clare, on the Rock Island Railroad north and west of Ft. Dodge.

Clare, named for Clare County in Ireland, had many Irish residents. It reached its peak around 1910-1920, and at its peak had banks, a grain elevator, hardware and food stores, taverns, a doctor or two, St. Matthews Catholic Church, an opera house, and other commercial services. If anyone wanted more, they would often take the train to Fort Dodge, or use a buggy for a trip there of several hours.

Barnum was named for a brother of the famous P.T. Barnum, who was involved with the railroad, and was smaller than Clare. It had St. Joseph's Catholic Church, a grain elevator, taverns, grocery stores, a bank and an opera house. Again, several Irish settled in and around Barnum. In addition to the Irish around Clare and Barnum, several Germans, Swedes, Norwegians and other persons of other nationalities settled in the area.

Manson was located in Calhoun County that abutted Webster County. It was considerably larger than Barnum and Clare, with a larger shopping area around it. Many settlers in Manson were of German background.

Before Clare and Barnum existed and before the final routes of the railroads were decided, there was a relatively large collection of Irish settlers west of Clare and north and west of Barnum. They had hoped to get a railroad to come to the area they had picked to build a Catholic church, but it was not to be. However, the church was built, known as St. Patrick's on the Lizard. This is where my mother's family members attended, and where they are buried in an old cemetery. The church itself is no longer there.

In recent years the number of Catholic churches around Fort Dodge has been reduced, with the closing of several. Among those closed were those in Clare and Barnum. The diocese of Sioux City is trying to build a new centrally located church. All of this is a reflection of a fall off in rural population, and the ease in driving.

Several non-Catholic churches were also built in the countryside, some of which remain standing and in use. In the past few years, with a decline in the rural population, some of the churches have lost large parts of their congregations and have closed or merged.

Transportation Was Vital

A most important need for development of Iowa was a good transportation system, and as noted over the years railroads were built across the state and in the Fort Dodge area and served to connect Iowa with all the major American cities and ports. Fort Dodge had many daily trains running through it from around 1880 to after World War II, and passengers could easily come to Fort Dodge from the nearby farms and towns. From there they could go by railroad to Chicago, Des Moines, St. Louis, Minneapolis, Omaha and other places.

Beyond the passenger trains, the freight trains operated on the same tracks and were invaluable to help farmers, miners and manufacturers move freight from one place to another. My Francois family used the railroads to move from Wisconsin to Nebraska, Nebraska to Louisiana, Louisiana to Oklahoma, and Oklahoma to the Fort Dodge area, each time loading up their wagons, farm equipment, and farm animals. Such movements were commonplace through World War I. In the era before highways, 18-wheeler semi-trailers and airlines, the railroads provided the transportation needed by Americans. World War I saw the peak of America's railroad expansion, and in the following years the role of railroads declined. In 1917 there were over 50 freight trains serving Fort Dodge every day, and over 70 passenger trains including the major lines and the interurban trains. There is still freight service to Fort Dodge, but the last passenger train stopped running in 1969.

A major asset of the Fort Dodge area was and is large deposits of gypsum rock and limestone. Today these gypsum deposits provide the United States with much of the wallboard used in building houses and other buildings. While a lot of wallboard is today moved over the highways by semi-trailer trucks, in earlier days the railroads made exploitation of the gypsum possible.

Iowa's Roads

The early roads of Iowa were primitive, and especially when the rains came and they turned to mud. Not just ordinary mud, but a sticky Iowa muck that it was almost impossible to drive through and which was noted nationally for its awfulness. In the winter the roads were rutted, and when the ruts froze the result was almost impossible to drive over. The old Ford Model T and most other cars had a high clearance to help their movement over the roads. Something had to be done, especially as automobiles and trucks became more common after 1900.

The initial roads in Iowa, as in most areas of the United States, were often the marked trails used by the Native Americans and bore little resemblance to today's roads. As people moved across America, they would make new trails that later got turned into roads. Once governments were formed, the Counties took on responsibility for their roads. Bridges were a difficult problem because of a shortage of engineers and funding. Often the people searched for shallow areas in streams where fords could be identified, and the trails or roads were laid out to make use of such fords.

Traveling these primitive roads on foot or by horse was one thing. Trying to move over them with a motorcar was another matter, and often caused real problems that became worse in the 1890s as cars were introduced in larger numbers. In state after state the legislatures decided that they should take a role, and the first state highway departments were formed in the 1890s.

Along with other States Iowa established a State highway system in the early 1900s, a system which in the early days consisted at best of poorly graded rights of way covered with gravel. These roads interconnected Fort Dodge with other cities across the State, and with neighboring States.

At the local level, roads were commonly made on what were called section lines, the place where one 640-acre section of land abutted against another section. The farmers were expected to help maintain these local roads, and I remember seeing Pa's horse drawn grader that he used when called upon to help improve the road.

In the early days highways just kind of happened. I recall Pa telling me about a trip to Minneapolis-St. Paul they made by car from Ft. Dodge around 1920. There were no maps, no numbered system and some roads had no markings and were really just farm access lanes. The first time they went they drove across farms on whatever roads they could find, asking people where the next town was, how far they had to go, and road conditions. Next time, they knew the way. As time went on, Iowa and other states created maps that showed highway locations, and route numbers were added to make it easier to give and understand directions to specific destinations.

"Mr. Highways" Got His Start in Iowa

Thomas Harris MacDonald was born in Colorado, but came to Iowa State College in 1884 where he earned a degree in civil engineering in 1904, and then joined the faculty. He took an early interest in Iowa's highways, and developed concepts of design and sound contracting methods. The Iowa Legislature, concerned about the problems with Iowa's highways, named MacDonald as

State highway engineer and established a State Highway Commission. McDonald attacked and cleaned up problems with bidding on road contracts, instituted research into road design and construction, and created a highly respected agency. His reputation was national, and in 1919 he was called to Washington to be the Chief of the Bureau of Pubic Roads, today's Federal Highway Administration. He held that position until retiring in 1953, and was then truly "Mr. Highways" for the United Sates. Under his leadership the Federal aid highway program was established and continues to this day. I never met MacDonald, but was deeply influenced by his achievements. In particular, MacDonald was a key player in creating the American Association of State Highway Officials (AASHO) in 1914 and in developing it into an internationally respected organization. I served as the Executive Director of AASHO (now the American Association of State Highway and Transportation Officials) for over 19 years, and felt his decisions and guidance every day.

By the 1920s Iowa had a good transportation system, including State highways, county roads, and an extensive railroad system. All of this supported farming and industrial activities, and gave the people a good travel system to use for shopping, for social reasons, and to help earn a living. As the decades went by the ease of travel by highway, however, encouraged people to drive often to the larger towns where choices were greater than in the local towns. Over time many small towns more or less simply dried up. The years when I was a boy growing up in Iowa the small towns were still doing pretty well, however, and we often went to them, as well as to Fort Dodge.

The McDonough's in the family Hudson – 1924
Front seat, left to right: Leo & my Grandfather
Back seat, left to right: My Grandmother, Irene and Alice

2

My Family and the People of the Fort Dodge Area

Those people who became Iowans were well settled by the 1920s. Some worked in the towns, making, selling and transporting things, offering legal and medical services, teaching, or performing other money-earning work. Others were farmers, or engaged in mining coal, limestone and gypsum. Several factories also provided jobs such as a glove factory of my youth, a clothing factory, a packing house for turning hogs and cattle into household meats, and some factories that made wallboard from locally mined gypsum that was sent all over the nation. Some farm machinery and similar equipment was made in Fort Dodge over the years.

Industrial development in Iowa in those days was often centered on farm equipment, with the John Deere Company headquartered in Waterloo as a prime example. There were several other tractor companies, but competition was rough. Iowa also produced other goods, such as the washing machines built by the Maytag Company in Newton, Iowa, which was sold to another company recently. I spent the summer of my freshman year at Iowa State working for the Lundell Manufacturing Company in Cherokee, Iowa. It started by building hydraulic operated wagons, and then moved into hay harvesting and processing equipment, which later took them into trash recycling machines. We will hear more on Lundell later.

As an aside, the gypsum deposits just outside Ft. Dodge were key to one of the largest national hoaxes in the late 1800s. A showman cut a large slab of gypsum out of the ground in Fort Dodge and had it carved in the shape of a human. He then secretly moved it to a town in the east called Cardiff, where he buried it. Some time later he dug it up and claimed it was a prehistoric man. The Cardiff Giant story was all the rage, until a scientist proved it was a hoax.

The Iowa Farmers

Most of the people who came to Iowa were or became farmers. The Iowa soil is black, very rich and highly productive. Settlers could claim the open land by homesteading, or by buying it from the government, from other people who already had bought one or more tracts, or from the railroads, who often received land grants of open land from the Federal Government as an incentive to build the railroad. The settlers favored tracts with a stream running through it to assure water for themselves and their livestock, and trees for use in building homes and farm buildings and to provide fuel. The Federal land office sold land to those wanting it. In the early days the land was low in cost, but a lot of work was needed to get it into production.

To farm, the settlers needed more than land. In the early days they also needed a team of horses or mules, a house to live in and to help the farm family survive the cold Iowa winters, a barn or other buildings to house cattle, hogs and any other animals, and a crib to store corn in after it was harvested. Usually, it took many months and sometimes years before the farm was developed enough for a good life.

Farm families expected to raise enough food to meet their needs and the needs of their animals, called subsistence farming. But they also wanted to raise more corn, oats, and other crops than they needed, and eggs and other produce, which they would sell to generate income that could be used for other purposes.

The owners usually tried to borrow enough money from the local banks to fund their operations until the crops had grown and been harvested, at which time arrangements for paying the bank back were made. Tenant farmers have the same concerns about getting funds to support their farming activities, and also usually work with a bank. The U.S. Congress first enacted some laws in the 1930's to help owners and tenants meet their obligations, including some subsidy and loan programs that are taken up by Congress and amended from time to time in a farm bill, which is often bitterly debated.

My Parents Families

My mother's family was the first of our McDonoughs to come to Iowa, dating back to the mid 1850's. The Francois family didn't come to Iowa until around 1914 and first lived in Wisconsin in the United States. They then moved to Nebraska, Louisiana, and finally Iowa, farming in each state.

The McDonoughs

The first of our McDonoughs were Patrick and Terence, and they arrived in Fort Dodge in the mid 1850's, as noted above. Terence met a widow named Sarah Owens White, and they were married in Fort Dodge on July 1, 1861. Terence was born in County Galway, Ireland in 1822, and died on September 20, 1908. Sarah was born in 1831 in County Tipperary, Ireland, and died on April 2, 1896.

Terence and Sarah had three surviving children, Josephine McDonough, James McDonough and Francis Terence "Frank" or "FT" McDonough, my grandfather. In addition, records indicate that Sarah White had a child, John, before her first husband died and while she was living in the east.

Terence McDonough first purchased the north 40 acres on what is now my farm from the Iowa Homestead Company for $10.00 per acre in July, 1870. In September 1873, he bought the south 40 acres for $8.00 dollars per acre from the same Company. He then purchased an 80-acre tract across the road to the west, where he built a home near the Lizard Creek. Later in life he purchased another 160-acre tract, which had a mortgage on it at the time of his death. Thus, by his death he controlled 320 acres of rich Iowa farmland, a large holding in those days.

F.T. & Katie Anne McDonough

My grandmother McDonough's parents were Bernard Monaghan and Margaret Mackin, They were married in

Camp Grove, Illinois, southwest of Chicago, on February 12, 1872, before they came to the Fort Dodge area. Bernard was born in Ulster, Ireland around 1826, and died February 13, 1896. Margaret was born in 1840 in Drogheda, County Louth, Ireland and died on September October 29, 1885. Bernard and Margaret had one child, Catherine Ann, my grandmother, commonly called Katie Ann. She was born on April 1, 1874, and died on June 14, 1955. Katie Ann married Francis Terence McDonough on August 9, 1897, and they had four children, James McDonough, who died very young, Leo McDonough, Alice Margaret McDonough and Irene Frances McDonough, my mother.

Katie Ann Monaghan   **Leo, Alice and Irene McDonough**

Bernard Monaghan also purchased land near the McDonough land. Over a few decades both of my great grandfathers became successful farmers, and were involved in the community. When F.T. "Frank" McDonough was getting married, he built a new home on one tract of the McDonough farm, leaving behind the original home down by the creek. The new home was handsome for the time. He also built barns, corncribs, and other buildings that I recall from my youth. In fact, my brother Eugene and I were born in this new home, he on July 9, 1927, and me on January 21, 1934. The house no longer stands since it burned several decades ago.

McDonough House, Christmas 1919

Granddad McDonough had an extensive orchard planted near the house, and built a windmill to pump water and to run a direct current generator that made electric lights possible on the farm decades before electricity from a public source became available. He was a noted breeder of beef cattle, and was active in the community. Unfortunately, he died on December 10, 1934, and I have no memory of him.

My Grandmother, Katie Ann, I knew very well and stayed overnight with her many times, during which I met many of her elderly Irish friends and learned much about the family and the early days of living in Iowa. She inherited farms from both her father and husband. As of this writing my brother, Eugene, and I each hold an 80-acre (more or less) tract of the McDonough land that has been in our McDonough family for well over 100 years. I inherited my tract from our mother, Irene McDonough Francois, who received it when Grandma died on June 14, 1955. Eugene received his tract from Alice McDonough upon her death. Leo McDonough had also received a like tract when Grandma died, and he quickly sold it outside our family.

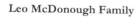

Leo McDonough Family

Katie Anne Monaghan

Terence McDonough also left an 80-acre tract to his daughter, Josephine, who gave it to a Catholic priest when she died. This tract was on the Lizard Creek, and was where Terence McDonough built his house when he first moved to this land. As noted above, my grandfather abandoned this location when he built his new house and farm buildings on land that was considerably higher than the Lizard Creek land.

The Francois'

My father, Rudolph John Francois, his brothers Bernard and August Francois, and his parents, Joseph Francois and Maria Francois, all came to the Fort Dodge area around 1914 and ultimately proceeded to rent a farm from Patrick Condon, located west of Fort Dodge and north of Barnum.

Rudolph Francois   August Francois

Brothers

Not all farmers own their land, but instead rent land from those who have it. The usual arrangement is that the owner and the tenant split seed and chemicals cost evenly. When the crop is harvested it is divided evenly between the owner and the tenant. Sometimes there are written contracts between the parties, but often reliance is had on the Iowa law governing such arrangements. An important date is March 1; if the tenant is moving to another farm, it must be accomplished by that date so that the next tenant can move in.

My father and his two brothers and two sisters were all born near Talmadge, Nebraska, where their parents were renting a farm and raised livestock, corn, oats and other grains.Our Francois family came to the United States from Weiskirchen, Prussia, now Germany, in July of 1846. In that month, after a 42-day trip by sea, Peter Francois and Anne Barbian arrived in New York with Elizabeth Francois, a child of Peter and his deceased former wife. His former wife and Elizabeth's mother was the sister of Anne Barbian, who wanted to marry Peter Francois but could not do so in Prussia because of the rules of the Catholic Church against a marriage between a man and a sister in law. Peter, Anne and Elizabeth traveled to Milwaukee, Wisconsin, where Peter and Anne were married on August 18, 1846 at St. Peter's Catholic Church in that city.

After their marriage the Francois family took up farming in Franklin, Wisconsin, a German Roman Catholic settlement about nine miles outside of Milwaukee. Here they had three children, the first two being Maria and Peter, baptized on December 17, 1846 and May 27, 1848, respectively. Their last child, Joseph, was born April 14, 1852, and he became my Grandfather.

Our Three Roman Catholic Nuns

Sister Mary Rose Francois

Elizabeth Francois is perhaps the most famous person our Francois family has produced. She was born on March 1, 1842, came to America with her father and Anne Barbian when she was 2, and lived with them at Franklin, Wisconsin. She had a religious upbringing, and entered the Franciscan order as Sister Mary Rose at St. Francis Station, Wisconsin when she was 15 years old. She moved through many positions in the order, and served for over 32 years as the assistant to the Mother General. Her fame comes mainly from her role in helping to start and then managing the new St. Francis Hospital in LaCrosse, Wisconsin, which today still is operating. In the Rose Conference Room of today's St. Francis Medical Center Hospital in LaCrosse there is a plaque that reads:

"Sister Rose was a co-founder and first administrator of St. Francis Hospital, a position she held from December 1, 1883 to her death in 1904. Her associates in inaugurating Western Wisconsin's first hospital were: Sister Matilda Lang, Sister Leonarda Hamentien, Sister Jerome Zwank and Sister Clementia Kelly. Sister Rose was exceptionally qualified by nature, education, and grace to meet the challenges that confronted her in the variety of positions of responsibility that for almost half a century filled her religious life. Throughout the years her name continues to be an inspiration and a benediction."

When her father, Peter, became ill late in life he went to St. Francis Hospital. I have a letter from the current administrator of the Hospital responding to my request that they search their records to see if there was anything in them about Peter Francois. The letter describes how Peter expired in the arms of his daughter, Elizabeth. Both of them are buried in the Catholic cemetery in LaCrosse, Peter in an unmarked grave, and Elizabeth beneath a tall monument to her memory.

Sister Mary Serena Schmitz
Our next nun was Sister Mary Serena Schmitz, F.S.P.A., the niece of Sister Mary Rose and the grand daughter of Peter and Anne Francois, her mother being their daughter

Maria. She joined the order on September 29, 1898 in LaCrosse, and became a teacher. She had an Iowa State Teaching Certificate. In her career she taught in 18 Catholic grade schools spread across Wisconsin and Iowa. During her last assignment in Superior, Wisconsin she broke her hip and was taken to St. Francis Hospital, where she spent a year. In 1964 she was transferred to Villa St. Joseph Nursing Home, where she spent the last five years of her life. Sister Grace McDonald, in her December, 1961 letter to the author, said "the name Serena was very fitting for this gentle sister." She spent 62 years in the classroom, and according to her obituary notice " she was an excellent primary teacher and was greatly loved by her little children."

Sister Susan Rose Francois

Sister Susan Rose is the daughter of Eileen Schmelzer Francois and myself, and is our fifth child. After graduating from DeMatha Catholic High School in Hyattsville, Maryland and Lewis and Clark College in Portland, Oregon she first went to Switzerland where she helped her brother Joseph and his wife Mary Lynne with their three children. She returned to Portland, and worked for the City of Portland for eleven years. During this time she felt a calling, which drew her to the Sisters of St. Joseph of Peace. Following a few years of preparation she took her initial vows in Bellevue, Washington in 2008, and her perpetual vows in November, 2011. She now carries out her work for the order in Seattle, Washington.

Susan's use of Rose as a middle name is mainly in remembrance of Rose Finan, a lovely woman that was a cousin of Eileen's mother, Eileen Schmelzer. However, when we picked the name I also remembered Sister Rose.

The Francois Sons Move to Nebraska

Leaving their father Peter in Wisconsin, first Peter and then Joseph Francois moved from Wisconsin to Nebraska around Nebraska City, where some relatives had already moved. Peter married Mary Burst from Wisconsin, and they started to farm and raise a family. The areas around Nebraska City and towns like Talmadge, Nebraska today have many people related to Peter and Mary Burst, as we found when we organized a reunion in Nebraska City in the early 1990s.

Joseph Francois, my grandfather, also started farming and looking for a bride. He met Maria Seifert, who came to America from Urnitz, Prussia in 1875 with her parents and two sisters, one of which, Johanna, was her twin. Maria was born on April 14, 1855, and died in Okmulgee, Oklahoma on July 5, 1949. She was buried next to her husband Joseph in Corpus Christi Cemetery in Fort Dodge, Iowa.

In 1935 Clare, Iowa produced the "Clare Souvenir Book," which contains an entry including a picture and text reading as follows:

Mrs. Joseph Francois – 80 years of age. Mother of 6 children, 5 living now. Born Dec. 14, 1855, in Urnitz near Bresleau in Germany. Her maiden name was Mary Seifert. Mr. Francois (deceased) was born in Wisconsin. Married in Nebraska, Mrs. Francois came to Nebraska from Germany at age of 21. Came to Webster County in 1917.

I knew Grandma Maria, and she used to call me "little Frankie". For years she lived with her son, Bernard, and then moved to Okmulgee, Oklahoma in 1948 to live with her daughter Bertha Schaller. As noted above, she died on July 5, 1949.

Joseph and Maria were married in Nebraska City, Nebraska on January 31, 1876. They had five surviving children: Marie, born July 24, 1885, Bertha, born August 21, 1887, Rudolph John, born July 24, 1889, Bernard, born September 13, 1891, and August, born January 19, 1896. Of these children, Rudolph was my father, and over the years I met all of the others.

Peter Francois, as noted, flourished in Nebraska and became a strong supporter of the area's Catholic Church. There are many descendants in the area, and in our reunion visit to Nebraska City we found many people who knew of the Francois family.

Joseph was less successful, and looked around for another opportunity. During our reunion in Nebraska I was told that he had some problems with the church, which wanted him to contribute to a Catholic school to be built near the church. He was living near a public school, and saw no reason to build the Catholic school when he was much closer to the public school.

After farming in Nebraska for over ten years my grandfather, Joseph Francois, chose to move with his family to Louisiana around 1900, where they learned to raise rice. Their home was near Morse, Louisiana in Acadia Parish near Crowley. Raising rice meant pumping a lot of water, and my dad had this role as a responsibility. One day he got caught up in the machinery and fractured one of his arms.

Rudolph Francois, at his home in Louisiana

After some 10 years of rice farming they decided to move north again, and first moved to Oklahoma in January, 1911 where they farmed and where my father, Rudolph, also worked in the booming oil fields in the state.

Their farm was located between Muskogee and Okmulgee. Dad said they were unhappy there, in part because of prejudice against Roman Catholics that they felt, and the activity of the Klu Klux Klan. They decided to move further north, and selected Iowa for a home.

Dad's father was not well because of a disease he had picked up in Louisiana, and the farm work was thus taken up by my Dad and his brother, Bernard, and for a time August.

Francois House, Morse, Louisiana

Bertha went to Louisiana, but was on her own from 1904. When the family moved to Oklahoma she worked in Muskogee, and then moved to Des Moines, Iowa. She met Otto and they were married on June 6, 1916, and had their son, Otto Henry, on May 8, 1917. They moved to Okmulgee where they established a home. In November 1938 they opened a small neighborhood grocery store in a converted garage behind their house, which they closed on November 22, 1952.

I never had it explained to me why the Francois family chose Iowa, Webster County and Fort Dodge as their final home. Perhaps Bertha focused them on Iowa when she moved to Des Moines, and there were also some distant relatives living around Carroll, Iowa. My dad told me that they farmed for a time in Missouri, but I am not certain where or when.

We do know that they were living in Webster County before January 4, 1917, because that is the date of a marriage certificate between Marie Francois and Richard Knorr, with Marie's address being given as Barnum, Iowa.

The wedding was held on January 4, 1917 at St. Paul's Lutheran Church in Fort Dodge, Iowa.

Richard Knorr was reared in Iowa, but was living near Makoti, North Dakota where in 1908 he had homesteaded 160 acres of land. Marie and Richard established their home on the homesteaded land. They farmed and reared a family that included one son, Henry, and two daughters, Esther and Erma Bertha. I met all of these people, and Henry lived in Washington when I arrived there and he and his wife, Lizette Fisher, gave me a lot of help getting settled.

Both Henry and Liz are now deceased, having died in Williamsburg, VA, where they went to retire. Richard and Marie sold their farm in 1947 and moved to Astoria, Oregon, where Marie died in December 1965. Richard died in a nursing home in Garrison, North Dakota on February 5, 1970 at age 92.

August Francois came to Iowa with the family, and helped with the farming. But he did not want to become a farmer and didn't like Iowa, at least in part because of the cold winters. After his father died in 1920, he went back to Okmulgee where his sister Bertha lived. He married a woman named Elizabeth, but it did not work out and they got divorced. He then met and married Marcella Park, who was also divorced. She had two children, Thane and Alto Park. August went to work for the U.S. Postal Service, from which he retired.

Bernard also came to Iowa, and he and my father farmed the Condon farm west of Fort Dodge and near Barnum; their father, Joseph Francois, was not well when they moved to Iowa, but lived on the farm with them and his wife, Maria. He had contracted a disease in Louisiana, probably malaria, and was weak when the Spanish Flu epidemic also impacted him.

Richard Knorr and Mary Francois Knorr

World War I

World War I started in 1914, but the United States stayed out of it for a few years. After a German submarine sank the ocean liner Lusitania off Ireland in 1917, resulting in the loss of many American lives, the United States became involved in the war by declaring war on Germany.

In response, the United States Congress set up a draft to raise an army to send to France. On February 27, 1918 my dad, Rudolph Francois, was inducted into the army, went through basic training, and was shipped to France and entered the front lines as a member of the supply company of the 33rd Infantry Division, a National Guard unit based in Chicago. He reached the rank of corporal, and saw action in the Meuse Argonne campaign. In his supply company his task was to carry supplies and ammunition to the front areas, which was normally done at night with wagons and horses or mules. He told me tales of some nights being under heavy German shelling, and especially of one night when a German artillery shell plunged into the mud right beside his horse and failed to explode. If it had exploded my dad would have been killed, I would never have been born, and this book would not have been written.

Rudolph Francois and Fellow Soldier in France - 1918

After the Armistice of November 11, 1918 Dad served in the U.S. Army of Occupation, and was stationed for several months in Luxembourg not far from where Peter

Francois used to live in the Saarland. He returned to the United States in May, 1919, and was discharged at Camp Dodge near Des Moines, Iowa on May 26, 1919. Like many soldiers, he told me he did not especially enjoy the trips to and from Europe, because of the rough seas. After discharge he returned to the home near Barnum and resumed farming.

Post War America and Iowa

World War I made many changes in America and Iowa, and many of them affected farming. First of all there developed a food shortage in Europe and some other nations, which helped raise grain prices to the benefit of Iowa farmers. The war also caused a large increase in automobiles and trucks, which grew in part because of their demonstrated value in France during the war and the wartime opportunities for many Americans to drive them for the first time. There was an increase in the number of telephones installed, and commercial radio slowly came.

In the closing months of the war Spanish flu began to rage across the world, including the United States. In the end, deaths from this flu caused about the same amount of dead as the war that spread it.

When he returned home Rudolph found that his father's health had gotten worse while he was gone, When we were in Nebraska at our family reunion I was told by some of the older members of the Nebraska Francois family that when they heard Joseph was very ill they went to Iowa to visit him, and to coax him back into the Catholic Church. As indicated earlier, he had some dispute with the Church that led to his leaving for Louisiana and falling away from the Church. They brought him back into the Church.

Joseph Francois contacted the Spanish flu, and died on April 21, 1920. He was buried at the Corpus Christi

Catholic Cemetery in Fort Dodge. August chose this time to move to Okmulgee, Oklahoma, where he went to work for the U.S. Post Office. Dad and Bernard then continued to farm.

The McDonoughs Retire – My Parents Marry

As time went on my father and Bernard came to be recognized as really good farmers. In the mid-1920s my McDonough grandparents decided they had farmed long enough and could afford to quit, leasing the farm out to produce income. They decided to move to the Minneapolis - St. Paul area, where their son Leo lived. They looked around to find someone to rent their Iowa farm, and selected my Dad and his brother.

As noted earlier, Frank and Katie Ann McDonough had one son and two daughters, Leo James, Irene Frances, and Alice Margaret. My dad knew these McDonoughs because of their moving in the same circles, and in particular he noticed Irene and was aware of her, more so as they agreed to operate the McDonough farm.

He told me that he used to see her driving her buggy into Barnum to take her music lessons. He became enamored of her, and after she moved to St. Paul with her parents he wrote her a letter proposing marriage. She accepted, and they were married at the Church of the Annunciation in Minneapolis on January 12, 1927. Rudolph and Irene moved to the McDonough farm, and Bernard rented the O'Connor farm a few miles nearer to Clare, where his mother joined him. All that was necessary for my appearance was now in readiness.

My brother and I were both born on the farm in the McDonough house, he on July 9, 1929, and me on January 21, 1934. Our parents did well on the McDonough farm until the economic collapse in the late 1920s, which first hit agriculture. The stock market crash in 1929 helped bring on a farm recession, and Frank and Katie Ann McDonough decided they could no longer afford living in St Paul.

Their solution was to move back into their house on the farm in Iowa, where my parents and Eugene were living. This did not work out well, and as a result my parents rented the Weiss farm east of Barnum on Highway 5, where we moved in early 1934 after I was born.

My grandparents moved to Fort Dodge, and their son Leo took over the McDonough farm. These depression years were hard on many people and caused a lot of changes in how and where people lived and worked.

The first two Chapters recite considerable information about the Francois and McDonough families. More complete information about both families will be found in the earlier publications about them, referenced in the *Introduction*.

Rudolph and Irene Francois - 1927

Francis B. Francois' First Communion
(FBF on far right, without picture, which he had already placed in the car)

3

The 1930s and 40s, and Me

As noted, I was born in the house on my McDonough grandparents' farm north of Barnum, where my parents were then living. That was on January 21, 1934, around 8:30 in the evening, I'm told. I followed Eugene by some four and one-half years. It was later that spring that my parents moved from that farm to the Weiss Farm, which they also rented. The Weiss Farm was on what was then Iowa Highway 5, some three miles east of the Barnum intersection with that highway. The part of the farm on which we lived was some 80 acres on the north side of Highway 5, and Pa also farmed another 80 Weiss acres across the highway and toward Fort Dodge, perhaps a half mile away.

My earliest memories go back to when we lived on the Weiss Farm. We moved from this farm in 1941, and the buildings were totally destroyed by a tornado in 1943. All that was left was the windmill water pump and the well pipe, which after the tornado was left projecting some 25 feet in the air.

I am not certain just how old I was when the events of my first memories occurred, or in what order they happened. After 77 years of life I just cannot sort it all out, if indeed I ever could. One memory, which I believe was the first, is of being in a house in or near what I believe was Minneapolis, when we were visiting my mother's family. I recall being upstairs, in a room where there was a horizontal door that closed over the stairway opening to form a continuation of the floor. I also remember a lot about the Weiss Farm.

The Weiss Farm was a typical Iowa farm, with a house for us, a barn for the cows and mules and the storage of hay, a corn crib for holding the corn after harvest until the moisture was low enough for shelling, a bin for holding the harvested oats, a garage for the automobile, a shed for holding machinery, a number of trees, and some other buildings, including a chicken house and a hog house. Pa had a few cows, and raised some pigs. The farmer's goal was to raise food for household use, and animals that could be sold along with grain not needed to feed the animals to provide income for the family needs.

It was normal for the farmer to also raise some chickens, to produce eggs for eating and selling, and chicken meat for eating. The cows produced milk for drinking and cream for selling, and of course they also produced calves. The hogs were for eating and selling, and each year we butchered at least one for the family. All of this required a lot of work, and all in the family were expected to help, as much as they were able.

Ma normally looked after the chickens and the family garden, which included potatoes, tomatoes and other vegetables, rhubarb, and other plants. She also did the washing and cleaning, and made sure there was fuel for cooking and heating, and water for drinking. There were no modern appliances for helping with cooking and there were no washers and driers. Ma had a wash tub that she filled with hot water heated on the kitchen range, which was used for cooking, heating the kitchen area, and doing baking in its oven, all with no temperature controls except the amount and quality of the corncobs burned for fuel.

Pa did the farming, plowing and planting of the fields, cutting weeds, doing any construction, maintaining and operating the machines, milking the cows and feeding the livestock, and harvesting the grains when they were ripe.

In the 1930s tractors started to appear on farms, and Pa had one that he used to pull the plow for preparing fields and for other sustained heavy power needs. But he also had a team of mules, Kate and Jenny, which he was used to farming with and which he employed to pull wagons and to husk corn, to pull the corn planter, and to pull the mower for cutting grain, hay and weeds. The mules also pulled a wagon for picking up bundles of grain and hauling them to the thresher, and to carry hay for storage in the barn.

Our house on the Weiss Farm was ordinary, with one bedroom downstairs and two upstairs, and a large kitchen that also served as a place to eat. We had no electricity, and relied upon oil lamps for light. My parents had one special Aladdin lamp that had a mantle rather than a wick and which gave a lot of white light. We also had some ordinary flat-wick kerosene lamps, which gave off less light. There was of course no television at this time. We did have a battery-powered radio, which we listened to a great deal. My folks liked to keep up with news events, and we normally had the radio on for breakfast, dinner and supper – on the farm, the noon meal was called dinner, and the evening meal supper.

As I learned to walk and talk I loved to wander around the house and the farm buildings and look at the animals. I remember playing with our dog, and using a rope swing hung from a tree. I loved to be with both Ma and Pa. One very good memory I have is of sitting in Ma's lap while she rocked me in her rocker, and we listened to music on the radio. One of the first songs I remember was a Kay Kaiser number about "three little fishies, swimming in a brook."

I enjoyed being with Dad and followed him around as he did things, especially to the barn and with the animals. He used to teach me little songs, and he could play a pretty good harmonica. One song he played well was "Turkey in the Straw."

Both Ma and Pa drove our automobile, a Lafayette, and I loved to ride with them. One special ride I remember was when I was around three years old, and I had a bad case of tonsillitis. Our doctor said the tonsils should be removed, and I remember standing on the seat between them as we went to St. Joseph's Hospital in Fort Dodge. I also remember being put on the operating table by the nurses, and being put to sleep. In the days after the operation, which went well, I also remember getting frequent dishes of ice cream.

My second visit to the hospital came when I was about ten. That day we were visiting Grandma Francois and Uncle Bernard, and they had prepared some popcorn. I had some, but quit eating because my stomach hurt. I told Mom that I hurt, and she said we should go to Ft. Dodge and see Dr. L.L. Leighton. The Doctor said it was appendicitis and sent me to St. Josephs Hospital for the operation. The operation was a success but recovery was slow, and left me with a scar.

I got ice cream again after the operation. Having ice cream was not easy for farmers, who had no electricity and therefore no refrigerator. What we did have was a heavily insulated icebox, in which we stored a block of ice purchased in Fort Dodge. I still remember when we got a large block of ice on a hot day in Fort Dodge, and Pa put it on the rear bumper of the car for the ten mile trip home. As we drove home I liked to stand up in the back seat of the car looking out the rear window, watching the drops of water from the melting ice hitting the hot pavement.

The 1930s saw the Great Depression, and as farmers we were poor. In those years farmers sometimes burned corn for fuel in the stoves, since the price was so low and coal or oil could not be afforded for household stoves. I can remember as a tyke being so pleased with my overalls, which had some extra pockets to hide things in, formed by failed patches sewed in place by Ma to stretch the life of the overalls. I thought it was neat, and didn't comprehend the pockets were there because we were too poor to buy new overalls.

In the 1940s all this began to change. But in my early years, this will give you a feel for our life on an Iowa farm of the subsistence kind. Subsistence meant we grew much of our own food, and that we were largely self-contained. We raised chickens for eggs and food, with excess eggs and chickens sold to raise money to buy limited supplies and such goods as furniture, clothes and the like. Cows provided milk to drink and cream to make into butter, or to sell at a creamery. Corn and oats were raised to feed the livestock and poultry, the cobs gave us fuel, straw provided bedding for animals, and again surpluses were sold for cash. Every day was a work day, seven days a week, with the cows having to be milked at the same time each morning and night if production was to be maintained.

The farm family members all worked. Pa did the farming, and most of the heavy work. Ma took care of the chickens, managed the house and cooked, and did laundry manually. Sometimes she also helped with the livestock, and she handled the books and routine shopping.

But the 1930s were happy days for us, and we prevailed. And Pa and Ma planned for the day when they would own their own farm, which came in 1941. They purchased a quarter section (160 acres +/-) one half mile south and one and one half miles west of Barnum. We moved there that spring, after Pa and Ma carried out extensive efforts to put the house and buildings in better shape.

The land had been in the hands of an insurance company, as were many farms late in the depression. Grandma McDonough paid some of the down payment money, provided the deed to the farm would be only in Irene's name.

By the 1930s the annual farming cycle was in place, and was followed by farmers with adjustments for weather conditions. In April the land was usually warm enough to be worked, and the farmer went to work getting the fields ready for seeding. The amount of seedbed preparation varied depending upon the conditions. Sometimes a field needed to be plowed to turn the soil over. Usually, the fields would be cultivated with a horse or tractor-drawn disc, which included an array of circular discs that cut and smoothed the soil. Then dragging a harrow over it, which in its simplest form was a frame with spikes mounted on it, smoothed the field soil.

Then it was time to plant. Driving across them and distributing oats onto the ground, commonly called broadcasting, seeded fields of oats. Any similar seeds were sown in the same way. Then came corn planting, which in the 1930s Pa did with a two-row horse drawn planter that had a trip mechanism on each side, connected with a planter box that held the seed corn. The seeds were dispensed according to the desired hill spacing by a mechanism that was actuated by a trip wire. Pa had to get ready for planting a field by staking one end of the trip wire at one end of the field, stretching it the length of the field, and staking the other end. After a trip of the planter along the row, Pa got off the planter, refilled the planter boxes with seed, and moved the stake at that end over to what would be the next row. Then he returned the planter to the other end of the field, and so on until the field was planted. I was always amazed at how straight and evenly spaced Pa's corn rows were. All of this was hard physical work, which in the early 1930's I simply looked at and marveled.

Threshing Time

In the summer the oats would need to be harvested, and in the fall the corn had to be husked. If the farmer also raised soybeans, these too had to be harvested in the fall. As a young boy, it was thrilling to watch the process for harvesting the oats, which was a community event.

Oats were a vital crop in those days, needed to feed horses and mules, and poultry. Usually, little was left over to sell, and indeed, as a cash producing crop oats were not high on the desirable list. Planted in the spring, usually on unplowed ground, the oats matured in early summer. After it was cut down and shocked, the neighborhood farmers met to plan the threshing ring schedule, based on the capitalist farmer who owned the thresher and the tractor to pull and power it. Horsepower was used to move and power the threshing machines until the 1920s, when first steam and then internal combustion engines became common. By the 1930s gasoline or diesel powered tractors provided the power for threshing.

Harvesting oats was both a single farmer activity, and a community activity where farmers worked together on one farmer's fields at a time. It started each year when a harvest arrangement was agreed upon, which was done by calling together the farmers who would participate in the threshing ring.

The planning meeting of the threshing ring was itself a major social event. The men gathered outside, normally in the shade, and talked about when they thought their oats would be dry enough to thrash. Out of this emerged a schedule for gathering at the various farms for a threshing session that usually was at least a full day or sometimes two or more, depending on the acreage of oats the farmer had. Meanwhile, the wives were also meeting, planning the meals they would prepare. When planning was done, lemonade, cookies and talk ensued, and sometimes a little heavier liquids were consumed.

The threshing day I will always remember began early one morning, as I looked to the west and saw a cloud of smoke coming down the hill running south from the James Dwyer farm, blowing over a slowly moving massive steel-wheeled steam engine pulling the threshing machine, followed by several farmers driving their horse pulled hay racks. On came the parade, until it came up Highway 5 and into our farmyard. Pa indicated where he wanted the threshing machine placed, so that the resulting straw stack would be where he wanted it, and the machine owner proceeded to set it up. He unhooked and parked the machine, and then blocked its wheels so it couldn't be moved. He swung out the large straw blower pipe and pointed it to where the straw stack was to be formed, and positioned the hopper to receive the oat bundles. Out came the very long belt that he stretched in a straight line from the machine. He moved the tractor so its powered pulley was in alignment with the pulley on the machine, mounted the belt, backed the tractor to tighten the belt, and proceeded to oil the machine with the same kind of long-handled oil cans we as kids loved to see train engineers use. The operator then fired up the boiler, and all was ready, with smoke pouring out the engine's stack.

While all this was going on, the visiting farmers and Pa had gone on into the oat field and were forking the bundles of oats up into their flat bed hayrack wagons, which had side frames adequate to hold the bundles. The horses or mules were trained to walk slowly through the field, as the farmer walked along from stack to stack. When the wagon was full, the farmer headed for the threshing machine.

It sometimes happened that in the days since the farmer stacked the oat shocks bumblebees had decided that the shock was a good place to nest. It was not uncommon to see the results of this, from a long ways off. You would be looking across the field, and suddenly see the horse team and wagon race off in one direction, and the farmer in another, flailing the air: a bee nest had been uprooted by the farmer's pitch fork.

The dirtiest job fell to the farmer chosen as the stacker, who worked under the straw discharge to shape the straw stack; but there was more than enough dust and dirt to go around, enough to please any little boy.

Meanwhile, in mid-morning the women and their food contributions arrived, and Ma had the kitchen range all stoked up and ready. The dining room table was opened out full, and any extra tables and chairs were set up. Pots of coffee were brewed, fried chicken was a common main course, and lots of potatoes and gravy, and pies and cakes. About noon threshing was closed down, and the farmers came in. First stop was to wash off the morning grime, done at a washing station set up outside with buckets of water, basins, soap and hanging towels. Then came the meal, and conversation; but not too much, since everyone had to go back to work.

Corn Husking and Shelling

Harvesting corn was a labor-intensive activity. First, the ears of corn had to be collected, which in the early 1930's was still done by hand, one ear at a time. The temperature could be cold, and it was usually still dark when the farmer had completed his morning chores and went to pick corn.

I still remember my father driving out of the gate, a kerosene lantern hanging from the high point of the so called "bang-board" temporarily mounted on one side of the wagon box. The bang-board was aptly named, since there was a "bang" each time the farmer tossed an ear of corn against it after having taken it off a stock and stripped the husk off the ear using a hook mounted on the palm of one of his hands. The bang-board guided the ear to fall into the box, which would be filled one ear at a time as the farmer moved down the cornrows. Today the only place we hear of a "bang-board" is in the sport of basketball, where the basket is mounted on an elevated vertical bang-board and serves as a target for the player to hit with a basketball with the intent of scoring. I don't know if basketball acquired the term bang-board from corn huskers or not, but it is possible.

A farmer's skill at corn husking was the stuff of legends, and local, state and national contests among farmers were common. Husking gloves were worn to protect the hands, and one hand had a metal husking hook carried on a leather band strapped to it. The farmer would grab the ear of corn and break it off the stalk with one hand, use the husking hook on the other hand to strip away the husk while the first hand held the ear, and would then toss the ear mostly devoid of its initially protecting husk against the bang-board mounted on the opposite side of the wagon box from where the farmer was standing, with the ears dropping into the box and slowly filling it. Some farmers could perform this husking operation with blinding speed, and would compete in and win husking contests. This era is gone, but is remembered by such things as the nickname of the University of Nebraska football team, "the corn huskers" and by the use of "corn huskers" as part of the trademark for a venerable and effective hand lotion designed originally to ease the pain of farmers. The need for husking gloves generated local factories, including one in Ft. Dodge, IA, that is long since history.

Pa, to the best of my knowledge, was never a champion corn husker. But he was persistent and worked at a steady pace, getting a wagon load of corn by noon. He would come home then, and first started up the mechanical elevator driven by the mules or the tractor and unloaded the corn into the corn crib. Sometimes the elevator would become plugged and had to be cleared, and once like many other farmers Pa got the tip of one of his fingers caught in the mechanism and cut off. With the corn unloaded Pa watered and fed the mules, ate dinner (which is what we called lunch on the farm), and then headed back to the field to spend the afternoon picking another load of corn. Before going out to the field in the morning he had fed and milked the cows and done other farm chores, and then repeated those chores in the evening after unloading the afternoon load of corn and before having supper. This routine went on for many days, and sometimes weeks depending upon how many acres of corn had to be picked and the nature of the weather.

The corn usually had considerable moisture still in it when it was picked, in part because the picking operation extended over many days so that the earlier picked corn was wetter than the last picked. To properly store the corn some provision had to be made for helping it dry out, and the corncrib was designed to do this. The corn crib might be a building with a roof and sides, with the sides constructed of horizontal boards spaced from each other so that air could blow through the crib. Or the corn might be stored in temporary cribs formed of spaced slates mounted on wire, set up with some sort of roof over head. The corn crib functioned between harvest and spring to store and help dry the corn while it was still on the corn cob.

Usually in the spring and sometimes later, the corn was dry enough to shell. Every farmer had one or more cribs of corn, and in the 1930s and well into the 1940s or later the shelling process was a community effort. One capitalist farmer had accumulated enough money to purchase the corn sheller machine, and he did custom shelling for other farmers. On the appointed day all of the farmers in the ring or group would gather at one farm and the sheller would arrive and was set up. The sides of the crib were raised if hinged, or boards were simply taken down, and the ears of corn were raked and shoveled into moving troughs that took the ears to the corn sheller. The whole process usually didn't take over a few hours, and if it ran over noontime the host farmer's wife was expected to serve dinner to all.

To a five year old, it was all exciting. And the huge pile of cobs left over was a wonder toy, good for many hours until Pa decided that you could well help to carry them in buckets to a dry storage place from which they were taken over the coming months to fuel the kitchen range and household heating stoves, and hot water heaters.

But exciting as corn shelling was, it could not really compete with oats threshing.

Eugene, Frank & Katie McDonough   Frank T. McDonough and Eugene

The Iowa Sketches

When one thinks back over the many years of their life, there are many events and happenings that will come to mind. The older one grows, the more stories accumulate. I have chosen to use these sketches to describe an array of things I remember, all of which helped to make me who I am, for better or for worse. The subject matter of the sketches is presented to the best of my recollection, as I write this in my 77th year. I may have some names and events not exactly correct, but what I have written reflects what is stored in my memory bank; and now, on to the sketches.

Movie Night in Barnum

In the summers of the late 1940s, after World War II and before the onslaught of television, the merchants of Barnum would sometimes hold a movie night. It was a great event, or so it seemed to me, to go to Barnum, talk and fool around with friends, and see a free movie.

Barnum had a single strip of stores in those days, arrayed to face a broad gravel road that dead-ended at its east end into the road into Barnum from what was then Highway 5. Across the road in front of the stores was a grassy area that extended to tracks of the Illinois Central railroad that ran parallel to the strip of stores, and a tree stood in the grassy area near the tracks. The screen was hung from the tree, and cars would pull up to the edge of the grass and park facing it. Other cars would back in across the street. Overall, it was an informal drive in movie.

Most of the people arrived in Barnum well before dark, to get a good parking place. We kids then played, walked the street, and went in and out of the stores to buy candy, pop and ice cream. Sometimes we would jostle around, as kids do, getting nicks and scratches as we fell on the sidewalk or the gravel in front of the stores. I remember one night when Ken Estlund fell and embedded a broken piece of a glass bottle in his shoulder, which left a funny looking scar.

The women would sit on or in the cars, wander into the stores, and talk. Some of the men did the same. The subjects related to farming - will it or won't it rain, is it too dry or too wet or too hot or too cool for the corn, will the hog and grain markets go up or down or stand still- and just plain gossip. Some of the men went into one of the two beer parlors, Harry Pierce's for the quiet ones, and Al Davis' for those who liked to talk and socialize more. In Davis' place there was usually a card game or two, and you could usually buy a drink of bootleg Four Roses whiskey.

As the evening rolled on, Davis' could get pretty active and noisy, which naturally attracted us kids. If a few of us went in Al would usually put up with us, especially if our dads were there. But if we got too loud, Al would gruffly order us out. There was no question that we would try to buy beer. Everyone knew everybody, including how old we were. But we could buy pop, peanuts and whatever else was available - except of course the whiskey, which was kept down behind the bar where you had to strain to see it.

The merchants jointly paid for rental and showing of the movie, and hoped people would buy enough to offset the cost. I think I always did my share to assure cost recovery, quickly going through the allowance Ma gave me for the night. The walking, talking, sipping and eating went on until well after dark, when the movie started. In these pre-television days nearly everybody then stopped their other activities, and stared at the canvas screen and strained to hear the sound from the loudspeakers. The kids who had stuffed too much in goodies into their mouths proceeded to settle down, feel sick, and doze off.

The Illinois Central Railroad then ran trains through Barnum, from Sioux City to Chicago. One usually went through midway in the movie, of course always at the best part. Blowing for the three crossings of the tracks in Barnum, the steam whistle woke up anyone who was snoozing, human or dog, and the falling and rising sounds of the roaring engine and rattling cars lingered on after the train passed. Sometimes the projectionist was alert enough to turn the movie off while the train went by, but often we simply stared at a silent movie for a few minutes as the loudspeakers lost their sonic battle with the train.

Sometimes the night train included a mail car, and we always watched for this. Each night the Barnum postmaster put the day's outgoing mail into a canvas postal bag, and strung it vertically between the top and bottom brackets on two horizontal arms on a large pickup standard mounted by the tracks. The railway postal clerk swung a pickup arm out from the side door of the mail car before approaching Barnum, and we loved to watch the arm snag and carry away the mailbag as the train speeded through Barnum, especially if you had posted a letter that day.

The strip included a grocery store run by Tom Hood, who was also an artist of some ability. His was the store I favored on these nights, or indeed at any other time. His pop, candy and ice cream was the same as Munson's grocery at the east end of the strip of stores, but Tom often featured something else these nights - his drawing skills. Looking back, he probably wasn't a great artist. But he was to 12 year old farm boys, who had never seen anybody else sketch their likenesses and many other tolerable scenes on a piece of paper.

Tom was a special Barnum treasure, especially when it came time for the annual junior and senior class plays. He did the theatrical make-up, and did it well. The other schools around didn't have his like. I was enthralled to watch him transform kids I knew into characters from other ages and places, and learned enough to become reasonably good at make-up myself.

Movie night in Barnum was special. In those post-World War II days before television they provided a wonderful time, or so we all thought.

The Barber Shop

Going to one of the barbershops in Ft. Dodge was always something special to me. This was male heaven to a growing boy, or at least this boy.

There were several barbershops in Ft. Dodge, and sometimes I went to one up near Karl King's music store on Central Avenue. But usually it was the shop in the half basement of the Wahkonsa Hotel a half block down, also on Central Avenue. The Wahkonsa Hotel was the premier hotel in town, named after an indian chief who once lived in Iowa. The basement had small windows facing the avenue, near the ceiling, and an outside entrance stairwell at the top of which was mounted the usual red and white barber's pole.

Downtown Ft. Dodge was a business center in those days - retail, and professional and other offices - and the cream of the traveling men stayed at the Wahkonsa Hotel, or the Warden Hotel next door. Some of these men were usually in the barber shop getting a hair cut, or of far more interest to me, getting shaved with lots of lather and a straight razor. Farmers in their clean town clothes and local men completed the cast, and the talk was all the man stuff a growing boy could want: baseball, Joe Louis, local, state and national sports, world events, fishing and hunting, and the smell of hair tonics, shaving cream, after-shave, and the male animal. Getting a hair cut was truly "heady" stuff!

Vacations

The word vacation is usually associated with people who work at a salaried job for someone else. Thus, as farmers my folks didn't usually think about vacations, since they worked for themselves and decided their own schedule. There was no boss to say, "You can take off the second week in July."

Now it was different for the kids. We had a boss, the school. We looked forward to "summer vacation," and vacation at Christmas and other times. In farming country back in the days of heavy manual labor there was also "harvest" or "corn husking" vacation from school, which for those who had to work on the farm helping to bring in the crops was anything but a "vacation." There were many farm boys, though, who much preferred picking corn to working on math or reading poetry.

If vacation means taking several days off and going away on a trip, then I did have some great ones while growing up in Iowa. After World War II, we drove to Okmulgee, Oklahoma during several summers to visit Aunt Bert and her husband Uncle Ott, Uncle Bernard, who lived with them, and Uncle August and Aunt Marcie. I was the navigator on these trips, or at least pa let me think I was. It was my job to study the maps, and select the highways we would use and the towns we would visit. We took two days driving each way, and so deciding where to spend the night in a motel was a major decision.

I was about 12 when we made the first trip, in the 1941 Ford that the folks bought during World War II. It was bought used, of course, since there were no new cars made during the war. The need for a different car came about when Ma had an accident with the Lafayette, in which thankfully she wasn't seriously injured - just some bruises and a small cut or two.

The accident happened around Thanksgiving, as Ma was driving to Ft. Dodge to pick up Grandma McDonough and bring her to our home near Barnum. Somehow, traveling to Ft. Dodge on what was then highway Iowa 5, she cut into a funeral procession and was hit by a car. The Lafayette was not repairable.

Buying a car around Ft. Dodge in the middle of World War II was an experience. Cars of any kind were hard to get, and dealers would patch up anything that could move under its own power and sell it. We heard of one man who on a freezing early spring day bought a vintage Ford Model T that looked real good. He proceeded to drive it out to his farm over the frozen, rutted gravel roads. It didn't look so good by the time he got it home. The shaking and vibrations caused by driving the car over the frozen ruts had knocked loose wads of painted putty the dealer had used to fill holes and dents in the fenders and body of the car. The rest of the putty came out when he drove it back to town, to demand his money back.

Pa was aware that dealers were doing what they could to get mechanically damaged cars to look and sound good on the lot, and thought he could sort them out. He missed the first time, though, and brought home a car that after a little driving poured out oil smoke and gave little power. The second time he picked the '41 Ford, which stayed with us for several years.

In our first trip to Oklahoma, we started early and got as far as Clarinda, Iowa, when the Ford overheated. We had to get repairs made, and then moved on south toward Kansas City on U.S. 169, where we shifted to U.S. 71.

This trip was my introduction to America's U.S. highway system, those roads built by the states with financial help from the federal government. Totally hidden from me then as I flipped through maps looking for the U.S.-numbered highways was that in 1980 I would become Executive Director of AASHTO, the organization that had assigned the U.S. numbers to these roads.

This was of course before the era of the Interstate highways. We traveled on two-lane roads, with lots of intersections. Part of the highway we drove on near Kansas City was paved with brick, something that fascinated me because I had never seen a brick highway before.

This trip was shortly after the end of the war, and things military were of great interest to a 12-year old boy. We saw a bomber plant in Kansas, and lots of military hardware.

Francis, Rudolph, Eugene and Irene Francois – May, 1968

5

Education: Barnum And Iowa State

My education began at the Johnson Township Consolidated School, in Barnum. The school was the result of consolidation of some one-room schools after World War I. The one room schools took children of all ages, and they were often taught by 16 -18 years of age young women like my mother. The Barnum school opened around 1923. It was built of brick and was able to teach some 250 students. It had two stories, a gymnasium with two dressing rooms, and a movable stage. It also had a home economics room for teaching skills to young women and a shop for training young men to use tools.

Given the rural setting of Barnum, the goal of the school was to teach young people how to survive in rural America. Reading, writing and arithmetic were the subjects we stressed, and we had English literature, algebra and other subjects, too. When corn-picking time came many of the boys took "corn husking vacation."

I am a Roman Catholic, and our public school accommodated us by use of what we now call "released time." One day a week we all walked up to a house belonging to a member of St. Joseph's Catholic Church in Barnum. Father James Shanahan was the pastor, and he instructed us. While we were being taught religion, the rest of the students had recreation time.

As I moved along in Barnum I enjoyed the course work and did very well. We had some good teachers, two of whom were Mrs. Joyce Gordon who taught English and home economics, and Wayne Peters, an ex marine who taught government and history, and also coached baseball and basketball. In my high school years I earned straight 'A's, except for one 'B', and much of that was because of these teachers.

I was concerned about the lack of any chemistry or science courses of study. As a high school student I had access to some out of the way resources. In particular I found a storeroom not in use, which contained some chemistry apparatus and equipment for physics experiments. I also found a few old textbooks. Apparently the Barnum school must have once offered these courses. I learned as best I could, and it opened my eyes to engineering. Eugene and I also read "Popular Science" every month.

I mentioned the shop. I used this quite a bit, and learned to turn wood objects. One winter Eugene and I bought a Shop Smith and installed it in a heated chicken house. The Shop Smith was a power tool that included a disc saw, a wood lathe, a drill, and some other tools. We took turns using it, and learned to make furniture and other useful objects

There were two subjects that occupied much of my time, magic and music, and through them the stage and big bands. I was about 12 when I got my first trick, which was taking a quarter and putting it inside a matchbox bound with rubber bands. I did this for years, and no one ever saw how I did it. Over the years I gathered a good magic act and while in high school traveled a bit and earned up to $75.00 per show, I also did some shows at fraternity and sorority parties at Iowa State. The key to my success was a wonderful gift one Christmas, some stage magic that became the backbone of the act. The equipment was ordered from the Dallas, TX magic company's catalog. I actually considered becoming a professional magician, and talked to Superintendent Ray Harris. He talked with me several times, touching on other professions and the loneliness of life on the stage. His arguments prevailed.

The Magician

As to music, Grandma gave mom an upright piano when we moved to our farm, and a stack of music, mostly from Aunt Alice. Ma found a music teacher for me when I was about 8 years old, and I took about a year's lessons and then quit. After another year or so I started again, this time with Alice Hacket, a nationally recognized teacher. I did a recital under her, and it went well. Then came the summer break, and I did not start again.

You may recall the musical "Music Man", where a con man named Harold Hill went to small towns and sold the people on starting a brass band. One day in June a man arrived at our house in his car, and Irwin Jones climbed out. This was about 1948, and Irwin sounded a lot like Harold Hill. He announced to Mom and me that he had been hired by the Barnum school to start a band in the fall, and he had been told I was taking piano lessons. "Would I like to play in the band, and if so, on what instrument?" After some discussion we picked the trombone, and he made arrangements with the Mid-Bell Music store in Ft. Dodge to pick out a horn. This was an important decision in my life, and it brought me into direct contact with Karl King, a world renowned composer and band director who years earlier had settled in Ft. Dodge after visiting it while with the band of Ringling Brothers-Barnum and Bailey Circus; he owned Mid-Bell.

The band went well, and after a year or so we started giving concerts. After another year we started to enter the state-sponsored band contests. We never won, but we got good experience. Irwin Jones also started men's, women's and mixed choruses at Barnum, and we did win some state awards there. I sang tenor in those days, and did well in contests. We also created a quartet, including Ken Estlund, Frank Kaputska, Dave Ritter, and myself. Irwin Jones asked me to join the Ft. Dodge Chorus that performed *The Messiah*.

For fun, I used to visit Paul Gurrnet, a neighbor farmer who played the piano in some bands in the area. He played, and I sang or played the trombone.

The music of my youth was that of the big bands, who traveled by bus across America to ballrooms to play. Fort Dodge had three ballrooms for a while, the Laramar, Expo Park, and the Bohemian Hall south of the city, which specialized in polkas and old time music. There was also the Twin Lakes ballroom open in the summer, and the Storm Lake ballroom. Often we would go in groups and did a little dancing and drinking, and lots of gossip. A complete list of the Big Bands I saw over the years is not possible, but the list includes Lawrence Welk, Tommy Dorsey, Jimmy Dorsey, Rus Morgan, Sammy Kaye, Dick Jurgens, Guy Lombardo, Ted Lewis, Frankie Carle, Six Fat Dutchmen, Malek Brothers, Jan Garber, Eddy Howard, and a number of local bands.

In our junior and senior classes we produced a play, under the direction of Mrs. Gordon. Our senior class put on "The Thirteenth Chair," a mystery in which I played the lead and also arranged two illusions for the production. I do not remember the junior class play, except that Mrs. Gordon directed it as well, and it was a success.

I did not play sports in high school, except for trying out for baseball. I caught for a while, but didn't measure up. I did become the scorekeeper and manager for the team.

In my junior year at Barnum I began to consider my future. The obvious goal for a farm boy was to farm, and I thought a lot about this. I did like being in the dirt. I also liked working with cows, and livestock generally.

But at the same time I knew how hard farming is, as a way of life. I also knew that Eugene was a far better farmer than I could ever be, and so I looked elsewhere. I have already told of my love of magic, and my decision not to go pro. I also thought about music, and joining a big band. But I knew that I did not have perfect pitch, which is important for a professional musician. I kept on looking for a place for me.

Come spring, 1952, it was time to graduate, and time for me to decide on what was next. I first decided on the law, and applied to the University of Iowa, which awarded me a scholarship based on my Barnum grades. But then I thought more on what I had been doing while in high school, especially the science and chemistry informal studies. I thought about how farming would always be part of my life, especially machines and raising things. And simply keeping up with life was important to me. Weighing all of these things, engineering came to the fore; I was also still weighing the pros and cons of becoming a priest, which was strong in my life between 12 and 16 years old. Aunt Alice got me some material about where to go to become a priest, which I studied at length. I finally decided that I belonged in the every day world, while supporting the church; in later days this came up again, when I was working with Opus Dei in the 1960s, and again after Eileen died.

And so, I applied to Iowa State and was accepted. I applied to study Electrical Engineering; I was sure from my years at Barnum that this would be easy. Boy, was I wrong.

IOWA STATE

Iowa State was officially called "The Iowa State College of Agriculture and the Mechanic Arts" when I registered there, and we had some 7,500 students. Today it is called the Iowa State University, with a student population of over 25,000. It was one of the land grant colleges created by Congress during the Civil War era. During World War II the U.S. Government put a lot of money into expanding Iowa State and some other schools to train men for the Navy. Included in the improvements was a large dormitory, Friley Hall, for men, which could house some 1400. It was divided into Houses, each named for someone famous. My House was Lincoln House for my first year at Iowa State.

The Friley Hall complex included a large dining hall, where most men ate. I earned part of my tuition by working at the dining hall doing one of three jobs, serving on the line, cleaning tables, or working on the dishwasher. My funding for college came from four sources, basic funds from my folks, a small scholarship because Pa had served in World War I, a small check from Grandma, and money from odd jobs.

In Friley Hall we also had a photography club, and a small radio station, KMRI, both of which I belonged to, I got pretty good in the dark room. As to KMRI I had a DJ show and was the music director. The experience of both was important later in life, especially in politics.

The trombone was important at Iowa State, too. I saw an announcement for tryouts for the Iowa State Marching Band and was accepted by Dr. Alvin Edgar. Every year the Marching Band went on a trip with the football team. This took me to Missouri, Nebraska, Colorado and Kansas State. We also marched in Des Moines for the Drake Relays, and of course the Iowa State VEISHEA parade. I also played in the Pep Band at basketball games. Like in Barnum, at Iowa State I sang in the mixed chorus.

Frank Francois

Iowa State also had a Greek system where fraternities (for men) and sororities (for women) provided housing and a social life for men and women who pledged to them. I knew nothing about this system when I enrolled, and therefore never took part. The Greeks were usually in leadership roles on campus, and ran a good social calendar. We in the dorms also had a social life, at a lower level.

There were also dorms for women, on the east side of the campus. The men's dorms were on the west side. Girls had to be in their dorms by a certain time and there were no visitation rights. A common meeting ground was in the Memorial Union, located between the men's and women's dorms,

Things were not always calm, however. I recall a year when we beat Missouri at home coming. The result was a riot, accompanied by a panty raid and an effort to block the express train that then ran through Ames. Photographers had a field day, and they sold prints to the national magazines; the next few weeks parents came and took some of the kids out of school who appeared in the magazines.

There were lots of stories about wild antics that occurred on campus over the years. One of the stories centered on a veteran, who was proud of his early Ford automobile. His friends noted he had left it parked at Friley Hall while he went home for a few days. They got together and disassembled the car, carried the parts to his room, and reassembled it there. When he returned the car wasn't parked where he left it. His friends played with him, and finally asked him if he had looked in his room. He looked, and was shocked.

One trick I did see was when some guys wanted to give a friend a jolt. He had the habit of coming in late, and moving around the room very quietly. When he went out they pulled the hinge pins out of the door and just set it in place. As usual, when he got back he crept up to the door and tried to open it quietly; when he touched the door, it was unhinged and simply slammed into the floor, waking everyone.

My first big surprises came when I purchased my first books, took them to the dorm, and looked through them.

They were all more advanced than anything I ever saw in Barnum. I looked intently at my 101 Algebra book, my first class. When I got to that class the professor announced that "You all had the first third of this book in high school, so we will start after that part." I knew I was in trouble.

Put simply, the farm-oriented learning we had in Barnum was not adequate background for learning at Iowa State. This was not universally true, with Mrs. Gordon's English classes having given me a basis for engineering English. But with no chemistry, advanced mathematics, drawing, materials and electricity, I was way behind, especially for   electrical engineering.

In our first class the Dean of Engineering addressed us, and said, "I want you to look at the person on your right and your left. Four years from now they will be gone." He was correct. I was not the only new student having problems, and a number had already left. I determined that I would make it, and secured a mentor to help me in math.

Some of my classes went well, including drafting, slide rule instruction, English, and chemistry, in which I earned a B. As I got into the properties of materials I did well, and found it most interesting. But math remained my failure, once I got through algebra. When I failed differential equations, I knew I was on the wrong horse.

That first summer I went to work as a draftsman for the Lundell Manufacturing Company in Cherokee, Iowa, responding to an ad for a draftsman to do parts drawings. My plan was to drive my old Ford car to Cherokee, and use it for the summer. But the engine froze, and the car died.

Unfortunately the car failed fatally between Ames and Boone, and I had to call home for a ride. Mom came, and the following Sunday we drove to Cherokee where I checked into a room. On Monday a Lundell employee rode me to work, and did so all summer.

Monday was spent going through the plant and looking at the parts that needed drawings. The job was doable but would take a lot of work, which I then got underway; that job took about a month to do. The question was what would I do next. Mr. Lundell called me into his office to discuss an idea he had for a new type of hay chopper, and wanted to know if I would lead the effort to develop it. I said yes, and the next two months were truly enjoyable. Mr. Lundell called in his key employees, told them what he had in mind, and that I was in charge and they should follow my instructions.

I drew up three machines, and tested them. The first two failed, although the chopper tooth I had designed worked. The third version solved suspension problems and demonstrated that the machine would work.

He took my drawings and went to Sioux City to see his patent attorney and in time the market version came out. What a summer it was.

When I got back to Ames I received counseling on what I should do with my career. It was clear that Electrical Engineering would be terribly hard for me, and that even if I got a degree what job might I receive. I thought about civil engineering, and decided to take some basic courses. I also thought about general engineering, which sounded like a good fit. As I had a few failing grades, I decided to attend summer school to make them up. I also kept up with my music and other activities, and looked for a good year.

A basic civil engineering course is surveying, and I found it great fun. Also enjoyable was a course in metallurgy, where I learned to weld aluminum. And over in general engineering I took a course in cost accounting, which didn't go too well.

That summer went well, and I picked up some of my failed courses. I also did some farm work, including putting up bales of hay on a really hot day. I had a lawn-mowing contract with a college professor. By the time fall came around I was ready to go back to school.

Year three went well, and I passed everything, For my third summer I applied for a job with the Northern Illinois Gas Company as a gas operating engineer, located in Joliet, Illinois. It was a great summer, with experience as a supervisor and education on how unions work. I also bought a late 1930's car, and spent weekends exploring Chicago, driving up into Michigan, and over to South Bend, Indiana to visit my cousin and visit Notre Dame. I went to some White Sox games with my fellow employees. As to the work, we blew up a house that summer, and had a pipeline blow up. While working on the pipeline I became frustrated that our workman was taking forever to unbolt a flange, so I jumped down into the ditch, took the wrench, and quickly changed the flange. The next day I was called into the front office and was told I had caused a union problem by jumping into the ditch; they had filed a complaint that morning. I pled ignorance of the rule, and that ended the matter.

I returned to Iowa State for my last year. It was fun and went by quickly. That fall was the annual excursion of the marching band, this year to Colorado by train. We took the night train and were in Denver by early morning. We then bussed to the hotel and checked in, following which we went up into the mountains and explored. The next day we played at the game, and then went back to Ames.

I signed up for a speech course, and found it fun. The next day the professor called me about joining debate. I agreed, and he said, "Where have you been?" He also had me give a humorous speech to an Ames service club.

About mid-year I started looking for a job. It came down to two choices; a manufacturing job in Denver, or a job with the U.S. Patent Office in Washington, D.C. I chose Washington, after discussing it all with my folks, Eugene and Aunt Alice. I now had a week or so to get Eugene married and get to Washington.

Eugene Francois

My brother Eugene graduated from Johnson Township Consolidated High School in Barnum in 1948, and entered farming with Pa. He was a member of the 133rd Aircraft Control and Warning Squadron of the Iowa Air National Guard, which was nationalized in 1953. As a result, Eugene was stationed at Erding Air Force Base near Munich, Germany for a year. After discharge from the Air Force, he returned to the family farm in Iowa. While Eugene was in the Air Force, I helped Pa farm.

Deciding to take up the traditional Francois occupation of farming, Eugene made plans and reached agreement with Ma and Pa on basing his operations at their farm. He then went to Wisconsin and purchased a herd of cattle and entered the dairy business, in addition to general farming with Pa.

In 1956 Eugene married Alice Mallinger, who was raised on her parents' farm near Clare and also graduated from Johnson Township Consolidated High School. After the wedding, they moved into a home they had built on the Francois farm, a home they enlarged and improved several times over the years.

Brothers: Eugene and Frank Francois

First Job Through Marriage and Elections

When my train arrived at Union Station in Washington that June, 1956 morning I was filled with excitement. I was about to enter the national Capitol, where my Aunt Alice McDonough lived and worked for many years, and near where my first cousin Henry Knorr and his wife Liz lived.

My first destination was to find a hotel, starting with the Raleigh Hotel on Pennsylvania Avenue, which Aunt Alice recommended. I took my suitcase, which gave me clothes for a week, and caught a taxi to the hotel.

My folks and I tried to estimate my expenses in Washington until my first paycheck, and they gave me that amount. Prices and wages were much, much less in 1956 as compared to today. For example, my one night at the Raleigh cost about $7.50. The hotel was not air-conditioned, and that first night I felt the heat of this southern town. After checking in I bought the three local newspapers papers, and started looking for a furnished efficiency within walking distance of downtown. One at 1630 R St. NW looked interesting, and the first thing next morning, I rode DC Transit to go see it. I liked it, and signed a lease. The apartment wasn't air conditioned, either.

When I packed for Washington I put all but my week's clothes in a trunk and sent it by Railway Express, which no longer exists. My next task this second day in Washington was to go to Railway Express and arrange for delivery of my trunk.

I had no meetings to go to for a few days, and so I set out to explore the town. For several days I rode trolley cars and buses map in hand, a technique I practiced in towns around the globe. Walking is also important and just listening to the people. An added concern in touring Washington in 1956 was that it had become racially integrated only a few years earlier, and memories of the "colored" and "whites only" signs were real. I could ride public transportation anywhere, stay in any hotel or eat in the restaurant of my choice. So now could any black, but many were not sure and hesitated to exercise their newfound rights.

The Patent Office

At this time the Patent Office was located in the Department of Commerce building near the White House, between 14th Street and 15th Street, and E Street and Constitution Avenue. I reported there and joined my incoming recruits. We went through several weeks of training, including the history of patents, principles of the patent process, Patent Office procedures, and review of how we were to proceed as patent examiners. We were then assigned to a Division where we began to work.

The categories of invention were over 400 at that time, and no one person could deal with them all. Instead each division was assigned several classes of invention, and the work was assigned to individual examiners. In my days there were three recognized classes of invention, mechanical, chemical, and electrical. Since then computers have created a new technology with its own problems.

To be a patent attorney you also need to be a lawyer, which was then my goal and that of most of my Patent Examiner friends. One can prosecute patents without a law degree as a patent agent, but these jobs usually paid less. As fall came and the time to go to law school approached, we discussed what schools we were attending. I found that most of those I associated with were going to George Washington University night school. Earlier in the year I had selected Georgetown law school. I was now faced with a decision, GWU or GT.

In those days getting into law school was much less difficult then is now the case; there was no LSAT, for one thing. My superior in Division 57 was a graduate of GWU, and he called the Dean of the GWU law school to see if I could be accepted. The Dean asked if I had my diploma from Iowa State with me, and I said yes. He invited me over for an interview, and after it he said I was admitted. I then cancelled my GT schedule and informed my new friends that I would be with them.

This GWU decision was most important for the rest of my life because of some new friends and the impact of the GWU Newman Club.

Newman Clubs like that at GWU were organized to help Catholic students in a non-Catholic university to meet and to carry out their religious obligations. There had been one at Iowa State, too, and I attended mass and did other activities. But my time was limited, and I couldn't do all that I wanted. As I started at GWU I decided to really get involved, and attended the first meeting of the year. There I met three fellow law students who became deep friends, Francis Richard Malzone and John Manning, who was also from Iowa, and Richard Wardell.

Among the new friends we met were older active lawyers who took an interest in law students, in part to attract them to join their professional fraternities. The three of us met Harry Glemser who recruited us to join Gamma Eta Gamma, an old time group that is now extinct. My friendship with Harry Glemser was to prove vital to our life.

I also found some others of interest -- girls. Through Iowa State I had few dates, preferring to wait until later.

Well, "until later" came that night. Not suddenly, but through a slow start I found the right one, not at the Newman Club, but an affiliated group called the St. Ann's Social Club that I also joined.

I got involved with the Newman Club program and ran for office. I also agreed to be a delegate to the Newman Club annual meeting in Columbus, Ohio, to which I drove in my recently bought Studebaker used car. It nearly died on the way over the mountains coming home, with a smoky clutch marking my pace. I also got involved in our region of the national Newman Club organization, which meant traveling to Baltimore, Pittsburg, Philadelphia, College Park, Slippery Rock, and elsewhere. For these trips I replaced my Studebaker with an Oldsmobile, used of course.

There is one other man whom I met in the Newman Club regional work, William Hansell, then a student at the University of Pennsylvania and National President of the Newman Club Federation. Bill went on to be a truly great manager of Allentown, Pa. After that he became President of the City and County Managers Association and went on to significant international honors. We worked together from time to time, and he and his wife came to my retirement function.

In the spring of 1957 I decided to move to the apartments where Dick Wardell lived, at 2141 Eye St. NW. By this time Dick had met Judith Kinter, who would become his wife.

As we went through law school we needed to target on where to take the bar. The obvious places were the District of Columbia, Virginia and Maryland, which had the added advantage that if you were a Maryland lawyer you could be admitted on motion to the D.C. bar. I opted for Maryland and so did the two Dicks. Because Dick Malzone, his wife and family already lived in Mt. Rainier, Md. This created no problem with him. But Dick Wardell and I had to move to Maryland. We decided to move in together in an apartment on Queens Chapel Road in Mt. Rainier. When making this move I expressed to Dick Wardell that I was a little concerned about a multiyear lease, since it seemed that he and Judy were getting along well and might soon marry, and he said not a problem. As it turned out, I was the one who walked out early to get married.

Law school required a lot of reading and analysis. My Iowa State degree helped a lot with problem solving, as did my life on the farm and my work with Lundell Mfg. The career of a patent attorney seemed a natural one for me, but after two years in the Patent Office I began to question whether working there for the rest of my life was what I wanted. The government green walls were closing in on me, as were the many government regulations. Most of all was the lack of personal goals among some of the older Examiners who seemed content to grind out the work like a drone. None of this was true in my Division 57 and some others, but we were in the minority.   And so I started looking around for a new position, one that would pay more and present new challenges.

After 2 years, 9 months and 3 days I left the Patent Office and became a Patent Advisor with the Applied Physics Laboratory of Johns Hopkins University, which did much research for the US Navy. At that time the executive offices of APL were in down town Silver Spring, and its laboratory was located in Howard County. During World War II APL invented the proximity fuse, an electrical device fired with a shell and which exploded it at the optimum distance from the target. Many army and navy leaders said the fuse was the most important invention of the war.

With a new job I bought a new car, an American Motors Rambler. I settled in at APL, and roamed the building in Silver Spring talking with inventors and innovators, providing patent advice and filing patent applications. APL was into surface to air missiles, submarine defenses, space issues, and many other areas. All of this was invaluable training for my work in later years setting up and helping to manage a highway research program.

With my new job, new car, and my room with Dick Wardell, my life was happy. Most weekends Dick Wardell and I would wind up at the Malzones for an intense game of hearts or pinochle, often joined by others such as Richard Haefs, Roman McClatcher, and Joe Chesanek.

As I said, I was a member of the St. Ann's Social Club, and went to a meeting one night where the Secretary was reading a list of new members. When she got to my name, she pronounced it in the French manner. Some people laughed and corrected her. Little did she or I know that within a year she would become my wife.

The Treasurer's report revealed that the Sunday night dances had been well attended, and that ample funding was available for club activities. With regard to activities, a picnic was scheduled for Ft. Washington in April, and a weekend outing to the Poconos in May, two dates that were critical to my future.

I went to the Ft. Washington picnic, and had a good time talking to friends and meeting new ones, and eating steaks and related food. Late in the day I wanted another beer, and went to the cooler. A woman was sitting on it, and when I asked her to move she said "no." I took a good look at her, and realized it was the Secretary that had mispronounced my name. She said she was Eileen Schmelzer, and then we both had another beer and talked for a while. I was smitten as her personality flowered, and asked where she lived. "At the other end of the world, in Hyattsville," she replied. I said that I lived close to there, and offered a ride home, which she accepted. And so our love affair began.

We dated heavily that summer, including the trip to the Poconos, trips to the beaches, and often just going out locally. Eileen had me over to dinner most Sundays. On an early dinner her mother served barbeque chicken, and then they had it every week. Eileen didn't find out I disliked it until after we were married.

Eileen Mary Schmelzer

Eileen was the daughter of Ludwig and Eileen Schmelzer, and she had a younger brother, James. She went to the local Catholic school in Hyattsville and then to the Immaculate Conception Academy in Washington. She then attended Dunbarton College until funds ran out. When I met her she was taking classes from GWU. She was a secretary with the Department of Justice, in the Internal Security office. In this task one of her responsibilities was to read the Communist Daily Worker and other communist publications, all of which were banned by the Catholic Church. She contacted the Bishop and was exempted from the rule, since she was working for the U.S. government. Earlier she went to Paris to work for the North Atlantic Treaty Organization, until her mother fell ill with her arthritis and asked her to come hope. At this time Eileen was engaged to a member of the St. Ann's club, but it ended a few months from when I met her. Later on her father, Ludwig, counseled me that they were really not in love, and that he and his wife were most happy at the breakup. In high school Eileen wrote a biography for the Schmelzers, and a copy will be found in the Appendix.

After meeting in May, we went out a lot. And we talked, and talked. Starting with religion, we discussed why we were both Catholic, and found that we had some devotions in common. We talked about international issues, Communism and its failings, the need to get involved in politics, that we were both liberals, although I used to be a registered Republican like my Dad until many discussions with Dick Malzone brought me to the Democratic Party. As I have told many people, I found that an Iowa Republican was really a Democrat but just didn't know it. My grandmother McDonough used to say "trust the Democrats – they are for the people."

We talked about having a family, and that both of us thought more than two children would be nice. We talked about our respective parents, what they did, and how long they were married. We discussed the need for more public housing, the need to get rid of racial discrimination, and other topics of the day.

By early August I was sold on Eileen, and introduced her to Mary Lou Malzone, telling Eileen that Mary Lou was my Washington mother. She approved of Eileen.

During the summer Eileen earned her driver's license. She took lessons from Mr. Moore, the father of Joyce, who married James Schmelzer early in the summer.

On August 15, the Assumption of Mary to heaven, on bended knee on the porch of their home I asked Eileen if she would be my wife; she said yes. We decided that since it might seem that we were moving too fast, we should wait a few weeks before telling her parents. We waited a month, and Eileen's parents were overjoyed. I told my parents by letter, and Eileen and I went to Iowa for Thanksgiving, her first trip west of New York and her first visit to a farm. All went well.

Now came the usual activities: picking a church (the parish, St. John Baptist de la Sales); the date (February 6, 1960); brides maids and grooms; rings; where would we live (in a different apartment next to Dick Wardell); who to invite; the reception – where and when; the Honeymoon, and so on.

For the reception we used the exclusive Congressional Country Club, where Ludwig Schmelzer was the Steward. As to the guest list, many people who were on it are still with us. They include Dick Wardell and Judy, Mary Lou Malzone, Liz Griffin, and Eugene Francois. For our honeymoon we chose The Homestead.

Our wedding night was spent at the Shoreham Hotel, in Washington. All in all it was a grand wedding. The temperature was in the 60's, but we were greeted by snow when we returned to Washington – and to a stack of mail, including the local newspaper.

Becoming A Lawyer – Final Steps

My last courses in law school were in the fall of 1959, and Dick Malzone, Dick Wardell and I graduated from GWU in February 1960, after our wedding. The three of us then drove to Baltimore for several months to a bar review course, and took the bar in late spring. The results came out in October. The common rule of thumb then was that two out of three would pass. Mary Lou heard from Judy and Eileen that Dick Wardell and I had passed, and was scared to open Dick's letter. But he passed – three new patent lawyers, too, a triple play. In October we were sworn in at the Court of Appeals in Annapolis.

The Political Life

Following up on the political discussions we had during our dating and while on our honeymoon, we said now is the time to move ahead. For one thing Jack Kennedy's campaign for the Presidency was underway, and this might help us get a start. I looked through the local paper and saw a notice that the Mt. Rainier Democratic Club was meeting that week. I went, and this was my formal introduction to politics. I met the Mayor of Mt, Rainier, a couple members of the state legislature, and several others. Mention was made of former Rep. Lansdale G. Sasscer, and the work to be done for the next campaign. Sasscer was a representative of the landed gentry that ran the county, and was regarded as the "boss."

In my research about Maryland I learned about the counties and the cities and how they shared power. Maryland had a strong Governor, who made many appointments, usually upon recommendation by the State Senator, of which there were was one per county, elected to a four year term. The House of Delegates consisted of a small delegation from each county. The one senator from each county made that person very powerful, especially if he and the Governor got along. All of this was changed by the courts when they stepped in on the one person, one vote ruling. But for the upcoming 1962 election the Senator was the key to power. And Mr. Sasscer wanted his son by the same name to be that Senator.

The son, known as "Gus", was a good lawyer, but he faced two problems. First, the incumbent, H. Winship

Wheatly, wanted to be elected again; he had been a strong State's Attorney who moved against gambling operations in the county, and was an independent, the opposite to what Mr. Sasscer wanted. Second, while wanting to do what his dad wanted, Gus seemed to be reluctant to run. A group opposed to the Sasscer Organization began, and Eileen and I followed its development.

At the state level the incumbent governor J. Millard Tawes wanted reelection. He had a strong organization outside of Baltimore, headed by a beer lobbyist from Baltimore, James H. (Jack) Pollack. He got along with Mr. Sasscer.

An issue at the state level was the state's approval for counties along the U.S. 301 route to license slot machines. In the corridor, which was then a major route from the east coast to Florida, the machines were a big hit, but local ministers raised concerns and the press joined in, as did Eileen and myself. Governor Tawes was pro slots.

We continued going to meetings around the county, and occasionally elsewhere in the state. We came to know state and local politics, including some of what went on in Baltimore. In Prince Georges County we collected some information on how the machine functioned. The lawyers were often key in arranging for zoning, and for arranging for water and sewer permits. Jesse Baggett, a member and occasional chair of the Board of County Commissioners, told me that the board's clerk would take a list of pending applications to Mr. Sasscer's office, and it would come back with a pencil mark next to some applications. Those were passed and the others were not.

The two political parties had central committees to consider party matters such as recommending persons for appointments. It was common for them to recommend themselves.

Turning to elections, the fact that you had died or moved out of Maryland didn't always mean you lost your right to vote. And if you drank and needed a little nip on Election Day, you could get one from a party worker provided you promised to vote the slate. This is a summary of how the county was run when we came on the scene.

In early spring Eileen went to her doctor, while I sat in our parked car – spaces were limited. I watched for her, and she suddenly approached walking fast, nodding her head, and smiling. Pregnancy! The Doctor estimated birth in the first two weeks of November. We spent the next few days telling family and friends about the baby, and making plans.

Among those plans was looking into buying a house. There were plans for a Levitt & Sons project of some 5,000 units near Bowie, which looked interesting. One day we took Mary Lou and Dick, whom we thought should also be looking at a house, and we all went to Bowie to look at the Levitt houses. We liked the rancher, and Mary Lou and Dick the colonial. Levitt had everything worked out on getting a mortgage at a low rate, with no closing costs. Building was underway for us to see, and the materials were good along with air conditioning. We found a lot we liked, and they promised a house in December almost in time for the baby. We signed up, and so did the Malzones. A lawyer named Edward T, Conroy maintained he had the first contract, and he developed a claim to community leader from this fact. The Conroys, Francois and Malzones were all part of many thousands of new residents in the Bowie area, most seeking a new, clean government.

David Hume Announces For Governor

David Hume announced for Governor in 1962, on a platform of ending the political machines power over state and county governments and outlawing slot machines, among other goals. A former treasurer of the Democratic party he was an international lawyer, and was a reformed alcoholic. He lived on Mt. Eagle farm in Charles County, and was active in civic affairs. Eileen and I found a lot we liked about Hume, and I wrote him a letter offering to help in his campaign. He wrote back inviting us to visit him, and we accepted. In our discussions we found much in common, and no negatives. We approached the Malzones and other friends, and they agreed with us to support Hume.

David introduced us to Sam and Frances Meloy, an old Prince George's family involved with the Hunt Club. They were two of the many people that were looking for replacements for Tawes and Sasscer. Slowly a new political force was forming. Eileen and I were in a leadership position.

Meanwhile, a new force was slowly forming in Prince George's County, built around the candidacy of Carlton Sickles to fill a new at large congressional seat created by the 1960 census. A liberal with a good labor record, Sickles was serving in the legislature and had many supporters. In December a group of his friends in Prince Georges began organizing a Sickles campaign.

Time Out For Joseph

In November Eileen was feeling strange one evening, and we sought the advice of Mary Lou. She said it sounded like labor to her, and she prescribed a long card game at their home. We did that, and at about 11 PM Eileen and I headed for Providence Hospital.

Joseph Francis Francois was born November 11, a national holiday. Neat! Or so his brothers and sisters thought. We had Joe baptized at St. Bernard's Parish in Riverdale; the priest who had married us was now stationed there. We got lots of presents, including a silver cup from David Hume.

In the spring of 1962 we decided to go to Iowa, to show off Joe. We drove in the Rambler, having fixed a bed in the back seat for Joe. We had an easy drive getting into Ohio the first day. Joe slept all the way, making driving easy. But then came the night in the hotel.

Joe was fussy from the moment when the car stopped, and Eileen and I had to take turns lying on the floor with him most of the night. When we headed east after a grand vacation we made noise to keep Joe awake most of the time, a much better result.

In November we were given a mid-December move in date for our Levitt house, and this took first place among our priorities. We were selected to be house number 141, if I recall correctly. The move went well, and the house was nice. Because it was mid winter the lots were all mud, however, and streetlights were not operating. Joe had a room of his own. When we lived in Mt. Rainier there were both lights and traffic noise, and both were felt in Joe's room. The lack of lights and the total lack of noise bothered Joe. So we moved him into our room, which solved the problem.

Offer To Be On The Ticket

In January the organizers of the Sickles Slate contacted me about running on their ticket, and asked if I would be a candidate for Orphan's Court, a probate court with three judges. One of the incumbents was a lawyer, and they said they would like one on their ticket. The law does not require a lawyer, but it helps for doing research and writing opinions. The major reasons for wanting me was our living in the new community of Belair at Bowie, and the work I was doing for David Hume. Eileen and I talked it over, and considered if we could afford it since the pay was small. We also conferred with David Hume – would this help or hurt his campaign. The three of us decided my running would be help for Dave. I would drop serving as chairman for the Hume Campaign in Prince George's County, and Eileen and Frances Meloy would now be co-chairs. I communicated all of this to the Slate. They accepted and I was now running for elective office.

The Democratic Primary

The purpose for holding a primary election is to choose those who will occupy positions on the General Election Democratic slate and to elect persons to party positions. In total 35 persons were included on the 1962 Prince Georges County Democratic slate, including me. There were some women among the candidates, but no blacks. For most of us this meant that this would be an historic event, the last time there would be no blacks running.

Farmers dominated the government in Maryland for years, and one tool was the unit rule. The unit rule required a Gubernatorial candidate to carry a majority of the counties, rather than a majority of the total votes cast.

With the ticket assembled, a campaign needed to be organized and some money raised, Royal Heart, a photographer and a candidate for the House, worked with other professionals to produce some campaign brochures on the themes "End Bossism" and new blood. Our campaign organizer was Claude Curlin, who worked for the national coal producers. We had strong support from the unions, especially with Carlton Sickles on the ticket. Our campaign fund raising netted under $20,000, a small sum. But we also had the support of the leaders of the

Washington Post, who wanted to see change in the County.

Eileen and I campaigned across the county, attending coffees and campaign events for David Hume and also for me. She did a lot of work on the Hume campaign, taking Joe along in his carriage.

Party Time

In March Eileen and I sponsored a campaign function in our house for Dave Hume and members of our slate. It was a success and generated some photographs that made the newspapers.

This party was held again the next year as our first St. Patrick's Day party, a party that continued for some fifty years. Monica and her husband Anthony now have taken it up.

Press Editorial

In the last week of the campaign I wrote a letter to the Washington Post endorsing David Hume. The morning before the election the Washington Post endorsed J. Millard Tawes, but right next to their editorial they ran my letter.

Results

In the election we won two of the five County Commissioner slots, and I won my position. Carlton Sickles won, as did David Hume in Prince Georges, Montgomery and Washington counties, but because of the unit rule he lost statewide.

November Elections

We then cranked up the campaign again and in November held a general election, where the Democrats who won in May won again sweeping the election. In December I was sworn in as the Chief Judge of the Orphan's Court, Chief Judge was because I was a lawyer, and the Governor made me his choice.

When the Sickles Slate was announced we released an over size printed platform document and displayed it. Among the goals was to end the practice of appointing Democratic Central Committee members to jobs. It fell to the Orphans Court to first implement this plank. We needed an appraiser to evaluate estates, a job that paid a fee on the size of the estate. A member of the Central Committee held the post, and he wanted us to reappoint him. We gave him a choice, either the Central Committee or the appraiser job, but not both. He stayed with the Central Committee.

I regret that once we won, the platform was pretty much forgotten. The last time I saw the oversize document it was laid under a mimeograph machine to collect spilled ink.

The Next Four Years

The next elections were in 1964 for Congress and President, and in 1966 for Maryland and the county. David Hume thought about running for the Senate, as did Joseph Tydings, the son of Sen. Millard Tydings. Eileen and I were heavily involved in discussions on the Senate seat, back and forth with David and Joe. David finally dropped out, and we backed Joe. One of the rewards of Joe's winning is that he invited us and the Malzones to President Lyndon Johnson's Inaugural Ball, which was held in the Mayflower Hotel.

Personal Problems

One of the impacts of the Orphan's Court was that I had to leave my job at APL. The Court sat every Tuesday and Friday, and APL wanted me five days a week. The pay for the Court was much less, and we had a money problem. I approached Harry Glemser of Bacon and Thomas to see if his firm had any overflow work to be done, and he said "yes". For the next 18 years this work combined with a few private clients was the backbone of our finances.

Charter Government

After the 1962 election I became very active in the movement to create a charter form of government for the County. The County had a Board of five County Commissioners, who operated under laws passed by the State legislature, laws suitable for small rural counties. Under a Charter the county is able to enact laws that are better suited for large urban counties.

The counties of Montgomery, Anne Arundel, and Baltimore already had charters. Efforts had been made to get one for Prince George's County, but were opposed by the organization. I spent many hours mastering the charter concept, and going to meetings and speaking.

While working on the charter movement I came to know Gladys Noon Spellman and admired her work. She had been a key supporter of the schools and well understood the county. Even as a minority County Commissioner she was able to get some good things accomplished for the hospital, the schools and the library system, among other projects. One of my fellow Orphans Court judges, E. Kathleen Shoap, was a lot like Gladys, and was a valuable ally over the years.

Integration In Bowie

The issue of integrating housing came to the fore in the mid 60's, and Bowie was a focal point because Levitt and Sons was not selling to blacks. A group of people from Bowie including Eileen and me picketed the Levitt sales office. The response from Levitt was that "we will not be the first nor the last to integrate."

After this a candidate for the presidency of the Belair Citizens Association, Homer Hammond, released a statement stating that integration may come, and we should talk it over. This resulted in a very large meeting at Duval High School, where the consensus on integration was not now. Ultimately, of course, the law was changed and integration became a fact.

Marie Eileen Francois Appears

In the middle of the Homer Hammond situation Marie Eileen Francois decided to be born, like her brothers and sisters at Providence Hospital in Washington.

The date was June 9, 1963. While I was waiting for her I wrote a letter to the editor of the local paper commending Homer for his proposal. From the outset she was involved in politics.

There were also some real family politics involved regarding her name. Eileen and I thought Ann would be a good name, since we met and fell in love at the St. Ann club. When I told her mother she exploded. Over the years her mother and her sister Anna had times when they did not get along, and this was one of those times. Knowing how Anna has treated us, how could you pick that name, she asked. So we rethought the name, and decided on Marie. Our change was too late for the District of Columbia, who had already issued a certificate to Ann, which we had to correct.

Getting On With Life

The Orphan's Court was interesting at times and boring at other times.

We did meet a lot of people, and learned much. After a year or so I knew I wasn't going to spend a lifetime on the court. Rather, based on my work in the charter movement and working on issues with the Bowie City Council I decided to seek election as a County Commissioner. This is where the power was to shape many key issues, and I had positions on many of those issues.

The next general election was in November 1966. I began to study public safety and the roll of police and our fire departments, the jail, our library system, and above all the public schools. I also studied land use, zoning and urban planning, and a host of related subjects.

And of course there was the need to campaign. This picked up as time went by, reaching a peak in the fall of 1966. My first task was to get on the primary ticket, again headed by Carlton Sickles, this time running for Governor. We went through a set of public hearings before a panel approved by Sickles. I came through this screening and was selected, mainly because of Gladys Noon Spellman, with whom I was appearing on the charter effort and other issues.

Michael David Arrives

On September 29, 1965, before the election, Michael joined the Francois family. September was hot that year, and it was a bit rough on Eileen. Joe and Marie were happy to greet Michael. His middle name came from David Hume.

Michael was interested in everything, especially schools. He used to take his little wagon a half block to the local school. After his first year in school he came home one day and said he didn't need to go anymore, because he had learned to read.

I Am Nominated As A County Commissioner

When the Democratic Primary was over the Sickles Slate had won three of the five seats on the Board of County Commissioners, Gladys Noon Spellman, Frank Aluisi, from District Heights and a civil engineer and me. Carlton Sickles lost in the Gubernatorial contest to George Mahoney, who brought open housing laws into the race with his slogan, "your home is your castle."

The General Election was wild in 1966, because of George Mahoney. Liberals were in a quandary. Normally Democratic, they rejected the "your home is your castle" slogan and supported open housing. The only option they could see was voting for the Republican candidate, who was the County Executive of Baltimore County, Spiro T. Agnew. In the end many liberals voted against Mahoney and for Agnew, who they thought had to be better than Mahoney. The liberals and the Republicans won. The Democratic ticket won all the other races in the county. As to Agnew, he quickly attacked the liberals and launched himself on the national Republican stage.

Organizing The Commissioners

Shortly after the election Gladys invited Frank and me for coffee at her home in Cheverly, to talk about how to organize ourselves when we took office in December. We agreed that the three of us would take control over the agenda, key positions, and appointments. We also agreed to meet again to decide what positions all five of us would have, and we set that meeting during an upcoming conference on the Metro system, to be held at Arleigh House in Virginia.

At the second meeting we decided Gladys would be Chairman for the first two years, Frank Aluisi for the next two years, and me as vice-chairman for four years.

Under the Commissioner form of government the individual commissioners often took interest in one or more agencies, sometimes simply as liaison and other times in a leadership role.

The initial assignments we made were as follows:

The Hospital	*Spellman*
Police Department	*M. Bayne Brooke*
Library Board	*Francois*
Public Works	*Aluisi and Jesse Baggett*
Recreation Department	*Francois*
Regional	*Francois*
Health Department	*Francois*

Bayne and Jesse were of course not happy with all this. On the morning we were going to implement our plan, Jesse wanted to see me. He had a counter offer – me for chair in years three and four, and him for years one and two. "Nice try" I said, but no sale. Our first session went well, and we were in business.

The Hospital Again

For the third time in my life I went into the hospital around April 1967 for an operation to relieve my hemorrhoids. I took some kidding over this. A few years later I had anther similar operation for a similar condition.

The District Council

Among our duties we also sat as the District Council to hear and decide land use planning and zoning issues. I sat a few days after taking office as the District Council for the first time, and I voted on the first cases in what would become over 5,000 cases by the time I left the Council.

Regionalism

I always believed that there is much to be gained through cooperation among governments. In the early 1960's efforts were made by the Federal government to have local governments form regional councils where they would work on regional problems, and the Metropolitan Washington Council of Governments (WASHCOG) was one of the first. In the late 1960's Walter Schieber became the Executive Director of WASHCOG, and went on to create a strong organization recognized as one of the best in the nation.

Since one of my areas was to look after regional issues, I attended my first COG meeting in December, and Walt Schieber and I hit it off very well. Over my 14 years as a county official I served on the COG board and served as

Chairman two years and President one year, I also was a committee chairman many times. I also helped create the National Association of Regional Councils, and served two years as President. I became a sought after speaker on regionalism, and traveled many thousands of miles. I also went on two Congressional study tours, one to Europe in 1972 (Paris, Helsinki, Stockholm, Warsaw, Budapest and London) and the other to South America in 1973 (Rio de Janiero, Sao Paulo, Brasilia, Belem, Altamira, and Manous in Brazil, and Bogota in Columbia).

Monica Irene Francois & Susan Rose Francois Are Born

Monica was born October 10, 1968, and Susan on July 27, 1972, my mother's birthday. Monica's middle name is of course my mother's, and Susan's comes from two persons, Eileen's great aunt, and our neighbor Susan.

Monica was always independent in her thoughts, and would undertake anything. When she was about three Mary Lou Malzone saw her walking with a bag. Mary Lou asked her where she was going, and she replied "Ocean City," some 130 miles away. Mary Lou talked her out of it, and brought her home.

One memory of Susan that I will always cherish relates to when I got back from the South American trip. Eileen came to the airport to pick me up, and she had to bring Susan with her in the car seat, which in those days hung off the front seat. Susan looked at me, who had been gone for two weeks, smiled, and then leaned on my shoulder all the way home.

We Moved

With five children our original Bowie rambler just wasn't large enough anymore, and we looked for a new home. We found it on Seabury Lane, and moved in July

1972, just before Susan came. We had lots of help from our neighbors, especially the Malzones.

Local Regional Activities

As part of my regional activity in Washington I was active in water quality and water supply and worked with several agencies. I was also involved with air quality, and again served on several committees. The appendices give more information on my involvement.

One of the good things about regional activities is that the local radio and TV stations like to put you on the air. One time a station had me on for a while, calling me "Mr. Franzwa." Eileen's mother called the station to correct the name pronunciation, and they asked who she was. "His mother-in-law", she replied.

Planning and Zoning

As noted earlier I was deeply into planning and zoning with the thought of making it better. The zoning practices in place when we took over were loose and uncoordinated, which led to many public arguments. Citizen Associations and to a great extent the charter movement were upset by what they called corrupt practices. As I saw it a big part of the problem was that we were considering zoning cases one by one, and not in the context of nearby pieces of land. I proposed a new approach where we would take up all the land in a given area, and do comprehensive zoning. The concept was adopted and is still in use. We also had very loose procedures when we came in, and we worked to strengthen them.

The Health Department

My liaison role to the Health Department was difficult to define, since the Department was in fact a state agency, not County. The County did have to help fund the Department. The Department did play an important role in developments in areas of the County lying outside of sewer service. Specifically, it could approve septic tanks for such homes and commercial developments if the test for septic tanks were passed. It was discovered that a number of septic tanks were approved even though they failed the tests. A grand jury was appointed to investigate the situation, and I was summoned. Later, the grand jury indicted the health officer. I found out later that some of the jurors were after me, and that it took a lot of explanation to convince them I had no authority to issue such permits.

The 1968 Riot

In April 1968, in response to the assassination of Dr. Martin Luther King, a riot broke out in the District of Columbia. I was attending a large Democratic fundraiser in downtown Washington that night, which adjourned when the assassination was announced. As I approached the parking garage the attendant warned me to be careful because riots were breaking out. The Commissioners met in Upper Marlboro the next morning with our police and fire leadership, and received a briefing. Thus far the riot was confined to Washington. And we took steps to keep it that way. We also offered to loan fire equipment and other assistance to the District of Columbia. We also sent some people to talk with leaders in our large black community to urge them not to get involved. We did have a liquor store on the D.C. line hit by looters, with one looting ending when a deputy sheriff tossed a tear gas bomb into the car.

That night we went up on one of our hills to look at the burning city – which resembled the pictures we saw of London during World War II. The next day the troops arrived, and we drove through downtown and looked at the damage.

Building Projects

The three of us saw the need for some building projects, and proceeded to move them ahead. They included some new libraries and firehouses, including a library in Bowie also sponsored by Sen. Edward Conroy and Gladys Spellman. Most of these projects moved along well. Three big ones ran into strong opposition.

The first project was a proposed new County office building, and Gladys proposed we hire a national architect favored by President Kennedy to plan the project. The architect saw this as the way to add something both useful and a landmark for the county. It was some 20 stories high, and the site would be landscaped and have much parking. It would also have had moving sidewalks, which became fodder for those who opposed the project. The public rejected our proposal, but when the new Charter Government came into office in 1970 they hired a Prince George's architect and moved ahead with building a new building. Unlike our proposal it allowed for only limited consolidation of agencies whereas our building would have taken all of the county offices. More space was built later, but on different sites.

The second project was a new jail. We proposed this in the late 60's, because the old jail was primitive, unsafe and overcrowded. The then sheriff was a strong supporter – but he lost in the 1970 election to a man who said the proposed jail was too expensive and not needed. The new charter government overruled him, and that jail was built.

The Industrial Airpark

The third failed project was a proposed industrial airpark, located south of Central Avenue and west of MD 301, capable of handling corporate jets and with prime office space for tenants. I was the chief proponent, and in the end the only proponent when runway construction was half done and the project was ended.

The project started one day when a local lawyer came in, David Ritter, and talked about the project, and its use to expand the County's tax base and to attract higher income residents. Frank and Gladys were supportive. And Jesse and Bayne were interested but concerned about public reaction – turned out they were right.

We hired consultants and they certified our proposed site. The site was ruled safe for operation with Andrews Air Force Base, and the chambers of commerce endorsed the concept. I spent much time speaking to folks around the county, but too little time in Bowie, where a group organized in opposition to the airpark. We recruited Winfield Kelly to support the project, which he did. This got Winny interested in politics. The Commissioners proceeded with the project, and let a grading and paving contract. This was during the fall election, and the airpark was an issue that made my reelection problematic. Gladys, Bayne and Jesse chose not to run, leaving Frank Aluisi and me. Frank lost, and I was the only one left.

The 1970 Election

The 1970 election was a tough one for me. The Democratic Senators formed a ticket called the Alliance For Action, and Peter O'Malley ran it. Well financed, they led our candidates in almost every position. I had named

Charles Ryan as my campaign chairman, and he called one day to say he had been recruited by the Alliance.

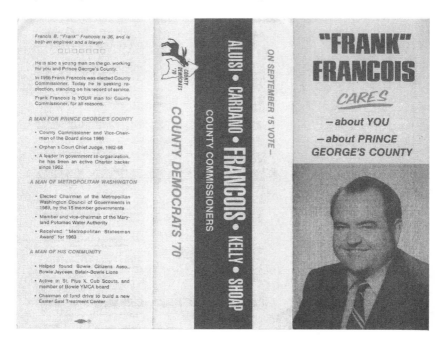

I called Judy Colbert, a friend who had been helping me. She said, "Guess we'll have to work harder." Her reply cheered me up, and we went back to work. Judy worked hard then, and for some 10 years as my aide. She remains a good friend.

That election night is one I will always remember. I was losing until the very last precinct reported, a black precinct on Central Avenue; also winning that night was the measure calling for a charter for the county. The charter writers established an eleven member County Council with five being the five Commissioners elected that November, which meant that I would be a Councilman. The four other Commissioners were Winfield Kelly, John Burcham, a Republican, Jack Garrity, and Francis White. The Charter called for a special election to elect a County Executive and the six additional Council members. Gladys ran for a seat among the six, and won. The full council met after the special election and as one of its first acts voted to stop the airpark. My "no" vote was the only one – even Gladys voted for the killing of the half completed project. The site was turned into warehouses and a County police station

MACO And NACO

Looking ahead, I decided I would get more involved in county government elsewhere and in Maryland. In Maryland we had the Maryland Association of Counties and the National Association of Counties covered the nation. Gladys had been involved in both, and I followed her.

Our first task under the Charter was to write and implement such things as a new personnel law, which I was involved with. Among other modern concepts, we wrote a gender free document.

MACO was where we met with our contemporaries, to consider county concerns about proposed legislation and other actions. We had a good Executive Director in Joe Murnane, from whom I learned a lot of use at AASHTO. One year I served as President of MACO.

NACO became a key activity for me after the 1970 election. I had attended the 1967 NACO meeting in Detroit, during the riots in that city.

I was active in NARC during these four years, and in COG. I also sat as a member of the Maryland Potomac Water Authority, and the National Capital Interstate Air Quality Planning Committee. I also got involved with METRO and chaired the Joint Policy Steering Committee on METRORAIL Alternatives Analysis Project.

METRO Ground Breaking, Judiciary Square, November 9, 1969
(Francis Francois is Center of Photo)

With respect to NARC, I was elected President in 1971 and again in 1972. There were two men associated with NARC that were my mentors in the years ahead, along with Walter Schieber and Bernard Hillenbrand, who was Executive Director of NACO. The two NARC men were Richard Hartman and James Dowden.

In 1973 I received an award from the Washingtonian Magazine, recognition as a "Washingtonian of the Year." The award included a banquet for Eileen and me, and was a welcome boost for the upcoming election.

1974 Elections

The 1974 election was a breeze compared to my earlier ones. The older children joined with their friends to distribute campaign information, and most of the ticket was the same. My ballot total was among the highest, quite a contrast with 1970.

In the next few years I got involved with some other national organizations, including the National Educational Development Committee of the American Institute of Planners, and the Intergovernmental Science, Engineering and Technology Advisory Panel of the White House. One of the benefits of this panel was a ride on an SST from Washington to Dallas, albeit at subsonic speed. I was also a member and President of the Community Association Institute, dealing with the associations nationwide that manage townhouses and the like.

I Become A Patent Attorney Again

In 1976 I became enmeshed in a patent application, this time one in which I had a one/third interest. It started when I got a telephone call from Ken Estlund, whom I went to school with in Barnum, Iowa. He reported that he and Paul, his younger brother, had invented the answer to the broken basketball goal problem that was causing grave concern in the pro and college basketball leagues. Ken had remembered that I was a patent attorney and wanted to know if I could help them. We arranged to meet in Washington, and agreed on how to proceed. I got a patent for them in August 1985, and we enjoyed a 17 – year flow of royalties. In 2008 I wrote the story of the Estlunds and published a book titled *Two Guys From Barnum, Iowa and How They Helped Save Basketball*.

Seeking National Office

After again reviewing my future I decided to seek the Presidency of NACO. This was a four-year commitment, with the need to run and win each year and in the fourth year run for President. I started the run at the NACO 1976 convention in Salt Lake City. From having attended NACO elections I knew I needed at least one flyer to hand out, as I traveled from caucus to caucus. I prepared a one-page flyer and ran off 500 copies.

In Salt Lake City I faced several opponents, some of whom came with slick brochures, trinkets, and several campaign workers. I offered a hard working President, cited some of my accomplishments, and talked about where I would lead NACO. I won the fourth vice-presidency.

1978 Election

The 1978 election was my last one, as it turned out. I led the ticket Countywide, which felt good. There were no big issues on the table, so things went on pretty much the same.

I did get more involved in METRO, and served on the Washington Suburban Transit Commission in 1978-80, and at the same time the Washington Metropolitan Area Transit Authority Board of Directors. We had a groundbreaking on the project then.

I was on the road quite a bit in these years, and I was growing tired of the work. One day while I was sitting on the METRO Board of Directors I was reading the American Public Transportation newspaper when I saw an ad for a new Executive Director for the American Association of State Highway and Transportation Officials. It interested me, and I called several people including Bernard Hillenbrand, Dick Hartman, Jim

Dowden, and several others. All thought I should consider applying for the position.

The 1979 NACO convention was held in Kansas City, and I was to be elected President of the organization. Eileen took the train to Kansas City, with Susan, Monica, and Michael. As incoming President I drew the second to top suite in the hotel; it was huge, and I called Eugene and invited him and Alice to come down and share the events. They came and we had a grand time. I rode back by rail with Eileen and the kids.

Being involved with NACO meant a lot of invitations. When the Pope came to the White House Eileen and I were invited. I was invited to the White House several times on issues like medical care, jobs, transportation, rural programs and other issues. We also were invited to testify in Congress.

The 1980 NACO convention was held in Las Vegas. Again, Eileen, Michael, Monica and Susan joined me. During my travels over the years, my children often came along. We spent some time after the convention for a grand family vacation, taking in the sights of the Grand Canyon and Utah.

After getting back from NACO I looked at the AASHTO job again, and decided to apply. I wrote a letter to AASHTO, outlining my interest and some background. This resulted in an interview and ultimately an offer.

Ms. Williams, President Jimmy Carter and Francis B. Francois

Leading AASHTO

AASHTO offered me the position of Executive Director at the initial salary of $55,000 per annum, to report as soon as possible. I told them I accepted the job, and that I wanted to take some time to arrange leaving office and some other details. They said fine, but they would like me to be at the Executive Committee meeting in August; and so began my new travel schedule.

In my first year with AASHTO I attended 35 meetings across the states, the same number that I made during my year as NACO President. At my peak of travel for AASHTO I was out of Washington some 140 days per year.

It was my plan to prepare a statement as to why I was leaving, where I was going, and when. I prepared the statement, and set the date for a press conference. Then somehow a reporter from the Washington Post, Margaret Shapiro, got wind of what I was doing. She called anyone who might have an answer. In the end she ran a story with the facts essentially correct, and which increased the size of my conference. Margaret was the brother of Peter Shapiro, the executive in a New Jersey county. A major factor in my review of the situation was what would be the impact of my leaving on Judy Colbert and Patty Smith, who worked for me. I urged Judy to apply to the Democratic Party for my seat: she would have been a dynamic Councilwoman. As to Patty, I was certain either myself in my new position, or another Councilman would want her, and so it worked out.

What Is AASHTO?

The full name of the organization is the *American Association of State Highway and Transportation Officials*. Its origins lie with the development of roads to move people and goods from farms to towns and ports. At first roads were built, if at all, by local governments. Then the states got involved, and in about half roads were being built and maintained. Local governments (towns and counties) also built roads.

By the mid 1890s three states had established highway agencies, and by 1914 this number had been raised to about half the states. In the early 1900s some private sector good road groups sent engineers to AASHTO meetings. Some of the states objected to private sector membership, and in 1914 AASHO was set up with no private sector members.

From the outset AASHTO formed committees on materials, bridges, and pavement, among others. AASHTO also worked with their Federal counterparts to draft the first highway bill, which required a 50% local match of federal dollars. Also, to qualify for federal funds the states had to create a highway department, which all did.

This was the basic AASHTO that I was going to run, under a Policy Committee that included one member from each state, the District of Columbia, and Puerto Rico, and an elected Executive Committee. My President, William Bulley (WA), gave me a briefing on current goals of AASHTO, including:

GOAL 1:
   1. The Organization Must Be Transformed From
   Mainly Highways To Give The Other Modes Parity
GOAL 2:
   2. The Organization Must Get Back to Engineering
GOAL 3:
   3. The Staff, While Good, Needs To Be Evaluated
GOAL 4:
   4. Communications Among Members Must Be
   Improved

He also told me about COSDOT, an alternate to AASHTO that some states favored. This was a direct result of the changes in state agencies, where Departments of Transportation have been formed in several states and was tied to an anti-engineering feeling in those states. He charged me with stopping COSDOT, which stood for Conference of State Departments of Transportation.

First Actions

The first thing I did upon taking over AASHTO was to hold a meeting with all of my employees, to introduce myself, and to give them the basic goals the Board wants me to follow. I then asked each of them to write me a letter telling me what they do. This gave me an overview of what AASHTO did, and told me who could write. Knowing from NACO and NARC how useful a weekly newspaper can have, I founded the weekly "AASHTO Journal," hiring a local newspaper reporter as the editor. It was an immediate hit, and over time it was highly regarded.

The August 1980 Executive Committee went well, and I got to talk one-on-one with some of the most brilliant men I ever knew. We reported the meeting in the AASHTO Journal.

Back in Washington, I met with leaders of the Federal Highway Administration (FHWA), the Federal Transit Administration (FTA), the American of Road and Transportation Builders Association (ARTBA), the Associated General Contractors Association (AGCA), and a host of other public and private sector organizations. All of us were interested in the next highway, transit, aviation and other Federal legislation, sometimes supporting and other times opposing. AASHTO is a 501(c)(3) organization for tax purposes which severely limits the extent of its lobbying. Also, some states prohibit their agencies from Federal lobbying. AASHTO responds to any requests from Congress, and on occasion has volunteered to testify on a given subject. My role was to keep up to date on testimony, to prepare it if needed, and to arrange for its presentation and any follow-up.

A key player on the AASHTO staff was Billy Higgins, our Capitol Hill and outside organization contact person. He and Sunny Schust weekly produced the AASHTO Journal, with my help, and the help of any staff member who was consulted in preparing the testimony. The goal was accuracy.

Like her predecessor Sunny Schust came to us from the press. She was truly outstanding, and wound up as editor of our major publications. She also ran a national campaign celebrating 50 years of the Interstate system. Sunny retired in 2011.

Early in my years at AASHTO my goal was to find a deputy executive director, one that knew AASHTO, had practiced transportation engineering, was a good writer, and with leadership capabilities. One day I decided that David Hensing was my pick. I was in Alaska and called him at home. He agreed to my offer, and over the years we were a good team. He also had a good understanding of budgeting and financial management. Dave was versed in traffic engineering and had a good knowledge of bridge engineering. When he left AASHTO he became Executive Director of the International Transport Association, dealing with electronic control of transportation.

My First Annual Meeting

An AASHTO tradition since its founding in 1914 has been an annual meeting held under the sponsorship of a member department, that is, a state department of transportation. This is a several year process, with the AASHTO staff visiting the proposed site and coordinating all arrangements. In 1981 the site was Las Vegas, the same town where my last NACO meeting was held during the summer. We had arranged for Sen. Jennings Randolph (WV) to speak at the opening General Session. He was the Chairman of the Senate Committee responsible for transportation. Mariann Humphreys, who was then our meeting coordinator, reminded me that Peter Koltnow, a well known lobbyist, was at the meeting. I met with him, discussed our need for a replacement for the Senator and asked him if he would do it. He said yes, and then we talked about what we would like him to cover. We also talked a bit about how the Senator can be long winded. Peter did a super job, and wound up by saying "and now, as the Senator would say, to my prepared remarks." The audience loved it.

Mariann continued to work for AASHTO for some fifteen years, running meetings, editing the "AASHTO QUARTERLY," and generally keeping things running. One morning we got a telephone call from her hotel, where she was working to check its suitability for an AASHTO meeting. The call was the ultimate anyone who is a President can receive – she had died overnight. We got in touch with her husband, and facilitated final rites.

Even after many years it is still hard to think about her death – she was a wonderful person.

The Years At AASHTO

The years went by fast at AASHTO. Our focus was on the goals, and we moved ahead on each of them. A few years into my term we had some feelings of discontent among the members, and I suggested we should engage a consultant to do a formal overview. The consultant, whom I had worked with before, telephoned all CAOs to get their evaluation of AASHTO and we underwent a number of changes. With regard to a return to engineering, working with the TRB and the FHWA we put together a $50 million 5-year research program, and implemented it. The list of achievements was long, and by my 65th birthday I was ready to move on,

I wrote a letter to the Executive Committee and delivered it to them during their meeting in Baltimore in 1998, effective on February 1, 1999.

There followed many thanks, summed up by a special banquet during the January 1999 TRB meeting. I extended my thanks to all who had guided my career, and to some key staff members. I have already commented on Dave Hensing, Mariann Humphreys, Sunny Schust and Ken Kobetsky. Bill Druhan, now deceased, kept us as a player with the railroads, and Otto Sonefeld came in following Bill. David Clawson covered transit and transportation planning. When Jack Stanton left us I appointed Jan Machis Edwards to coordinate our growing software development and she did an outstanding job. Hannah Whitney took over the meeting planning work when Mary Ann passed on, and did some great things. A quiet person is Linda Graves, who edited some of our most important works. Bob Cullen remains a valuable asset in finding out the details of projects, and although his career was shortened by a stroke Joshua Elks will always be remembered. All of my staff members were invaluable to me, and I hereby thank each and every one.

Upon retirement Eileen and I first took a week cruise through the Panama Canal, a welcome relaxing time. We did more cruises and visits to family. Like when we were courting we talked about the future, God, our friends, and changes to our home.

I was asked by Cambridge Systematics to join their Board of Directors. They have a solid reputation, and I was honored to be asked. I served 10 years, meeting four times a year, and felt that I did a good job.

We enjoyed retirement, until health problems affected both of us. In June 2002 we went on a cruise to Montreal with Susan and then rode the train to New York, where we saw two shows. When we got back, Eileen visited the doctor because she had a growth in her vulva area. He confirmed cancer and we scheduled an operation in July 2002. The operation was rough, but Eileen came through it. It was followed by radiation treatments and chemotherapy.

We then both came down with leg problems, Eileen's from diabetes and mine from osteoarthritis. Her problem flared up in February while we were in the mountains. I got her back to Doctors Hospital, and the Doctor said we had to remove the leg or lose her life. We did that, and by mid summer she was up and around.

One year after the cancer surgery, in July 2003, she went in for her one-year check-up, and the cancer was back. Eileen underwent another operation, with poor results. I brought Hospice into the situation and Eileen died on October 22, 2003. Her death was the low point of my life, and I cannot recover in this life.

As to myself, my right hip really started hurting during 2002. In February 2004 Monica planned to get married in Chicago and invited me to come. I of course said "yes," and arranged to go by rail.   When I got back I went to my doctor, and we arranged for replacing my right hip. The operation and recovery went well. Later that year, however, I fell and hit my head while visiting Ellicott City, Maryland. On November 3, 2004, Election Day, I was admitted to the hospital and underwent emergency surgery for a subdural hematoma brain injury. After the incident, my children helped me sell our home in Bowie and I moved to the Georgetown Retirement Residence in Washington, D.C.

Five years later my other hip started to hurt, and I went back to the doctor. He prescribed a new left hip, and we operated in June 2011. Recovery has not gone well, in part because in October 2011 I had another subdural hematoma brain injury that has affected my recovery,

So far it has been a great life, and much of it is based on my Iowa heritage. Growing up on our farm brought me numerous experiences that furthered my life and my careers. I loved working with the livestock, going to movie night in Barnum, the Circus in Ft. Dodge, the Iowa State Fair and the Spencer Fair. My summer with the Lundell Company gave me important management skills and patent knowledge. My musical training opened doors for me at Iowa State, and gave me travel experience. Iowa is filled with good, God fearing people who care about each other, which is why I say "Me? I'm from Iowa."

In many of my speeches across the nation I often closed with an old Irish blessing. Let me do the same here:

MAY THE ROAD RISE TO MEET YOU,
MAY THE WIND BE ALWAYS AT YOUR BACK,
MAY THE RAIN FALL SOFT UPON YOUR FIELDS,
AND UNTIL WE MEET AGAIN MAY GOD HOLD YOU
IN THE PALM OF HIS HAND.

Photos

Many of the photos that were collected for this book are placed throughout the volume. Others are presented here.

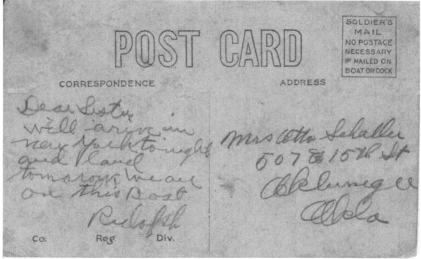

Postcard from Rudolph telling his sister he was headed home form the war on
the *S. S. Mount Vernon*

Francis & Eileen Wedding Photo

Francis Francois and Attorney General Mitchell

Francis & Eileen Francois and Gladys Noon Spellman

Francis Francois - 1968

Francis Francois - 1972

Francis Francois - 1972

Francis Francois - 1973

Francis Francois and Francis Aluisi

Meeting with President Ford

Vice President Mondale, President Carter and Francis B. Francois

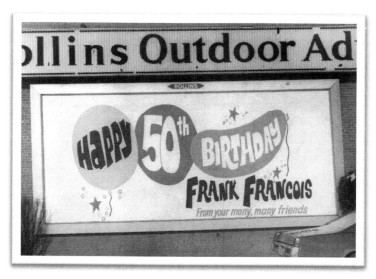

Billboard Celebrating FBF's 50th Birthday

Francis Francois at NACo Convention, Las Vegas, 1980

Francis Francois, Sugar Ray Leonard & Winfield Kelly

Rosie Greer and Francis Francois

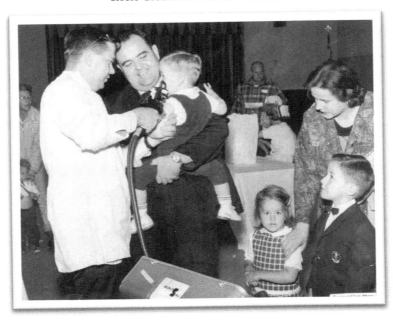

Francis holds Michael, while Marie, Joseph and Eileen Francois look on

Jane, Jennifer, James, Julie and Joanne Francois

Eugene Francois Family

Michael, Marie, Susan, Monica and Joseph Francois – Bowie, MD

Joseph, Francis, Michael, Eileen, Marie, Susan and Monica Francois

Appendix

This Appendix includes a *curriculum vitae* summing up my careers in law, politics, association management and farming, and lists a number of articles and presentations I have made.

FRANCIS BERNARD FRANCOIS
Curriculum Vitae

Current Activities

Retired from full time employment. Engaged in limited intellectual property law practice and limited transportation consultant practice, and in farming land in Iowa.

Professional Education

1956   Iowa State University
        B.S. (General Engineering, Industrial Option)

1960   George Washington University
        LL.B. (Law)
1960   Admitted to Maryland Bar
1960   Registered before U.S. Patent and Trademark Office

Employment

Intellectual Property Protection

1956-59 United States Patent Office, Patent Examiner
1959-62 Applied Physics Laboratory, Johns Hopkins
        University, Patent Advisor
1962-80 Bacon and Thomas Patent Law Firm, Associate
        Attorney
1980-   Private Practice

Consultant - Transportation Policy and Program Advice

1999-   Private Practice

Prince George's County, Maryland Elected Public Offices

1962-66 Orphan's Court, Chief Judge
1966-70 County Commissioner
1971-80 County Councilman

Academic

1973   Center for Special and Advanced Programs,
        University of Northern Colorado (Washington, D.C.
        Location), Instructor in Urban Systems Analysis
1974-87 Earlham College (Washington Term), Instructor in
        Urban Problems
        Seminar

American Association of State Highway and Transportation Officials
1980-99 Executive Director

Professional Affiliations
National Academy of Engineering (member, elected 1999)
Committee on Transportation History (ex officio member), Transportation Research Board of the National Research Council
Task Force on Transportation Asset Management (member), Transportation Research Board of the National Research Council
Panel for National Cooperative Highway Research Program Project 20-36, Highway Research Technology-International Information Sharing (member), Transportation Research Board of the National Research Council
Panel for National Cooperative Highway Research Program Project 20-7/142, Scoping Study for a National Strategic Plan for Transportation Information Management
Board of Directors, Honorary Life Member, Intelligent Transportation Society of America (past Chair)
Board of Advisors for the Center for Advanced Transportation Technology, University of Maryland (ex officio member)
Public Works Management and Policy magazine Editorial Board (member)
Task Force on Critical Transportation Infrastructure Security (member), Transportation Research Board of the National Research Council National Research and Technology Transportation Research Board of the National Research Council – Report issued 2002
Committee for Study of a Future Strategic Highway Research Program (member), Transportation Research Board of the National Research Council - Report issued 2002
Panel on Transportation of the National Research Council's Committee on Science and Technology for Countering Terrorism - 2002 - Report issued in 2002 by the NRC
Board of Directors, Cambridge Systematics, Inc. (past member)

Appointed Public Offices

1966-80 Metropolitan Washington Council of Governments, Board of Directors (Chair, 1969 and 1976, President, 1971)

1970-80 Maryland Potomac Water Authority (Vice Chair)

1972-79 National Capital Interstate Air Quality Planning Committee (Chair, 1972-74)

1973-74 Governor's Interstate Water Quality Planning Committee for Metropolitan Washington (Ex Officio member)

1975-77 Metropolitan Washington Water Resources Planning Board (member)

1975-80 Maryland Air Quality Control Advisory Council (member)

1975-80 Maryland Rehabilitation Loan Program Advisory Council (member)

1977-78 Joint Policy Steering Committee on Metrorail Alternatives Analysis Project (Chair)

1978-80 Washington Suburban Transit Commission (member, Chairman, 1979)

1978-80 Washington Metropolitan Area Transit Authority, Board of Directors (member)

1987-88 Prince George's County Development Quality Steering Committee (member and chair)

1990-2001 Industrial Development Authority for Prince George's County, Maryland (member)

National and International Advisory Panels and Committees

1975-78 National Educational Development Committee, American Institute of Planners (member)

1975-80 Community Associations Institute Board of Directors (member and president)

1976-80 Intergovernmental Science, Engineering and Technology Advisory Panel the White House Office of Science and Technology - (member) Co-Chair Transportation, Commerce and Community Development Task Force

1979-80 Local Government Energy Policy Advisory Committee, U.S. Department of Energy (member)

1980-81 Council on Development Choices for the '80's, U.S. Department of Housing and Urban Development (member)

1980-99 While Executive Director of AASHTO, served as an ex officio member of many panels and committees of the National Research Council (NRC) of the National Academy of Sciences (NAS), including:
- NRC Executive Committee, Strategic Highway Research Program Transportation Research Board (TRB) of the NRC
- Executive Committee, Transportation
- Research Board Research & Technology Advisory Committee
- SHRP Advisory Committee
- Subcommittee on Planning & Policy Review Panels organized under the National Cooperative Highway Research Program (NCHRP) managed by the TRB, such as:
- Project SP 20-36, Highway Research and Technology - International Information Project SP 20-24, Research Program Design - Administration of Highway and Transportation Agencies

1982-84 Steering Committee for a Strategic Transportation Research Study: Highways (member), Transportation Research Board

1990-99 Advisory Council for the Center for Transportation Studies, Massachusetts Institute of Technology (member)

1990-99 Board of Directors, World Road Association (PIARC)

1991-99 Board of Directors, International Road Federation

1991-99 National Center for Asphalt Technology Board of Directors (member)

1993-99 Highway Innovative Technology Evaluation Center Executive Committee (member)

1992-99 International Institute for Surface Transportation Policy Studies, Board of Trustees (member)

1992-99 Public Roads magazine Publications Board, Federal Highway Administration (member)

1998-99 Professional Capacity Building Steering Committee, ITS America (member)

State and National Association Offices Held

1978-79 Maryland Association of Counties - President

1971-72 National Association of Regional Councils President

1979-80 Community Associations Institute - President

1979-80 National Association of Counties - President

Professional Association/Society Memberships
American Intellectual Property Law Association
Institute of Transportation Engineers

Awards and Honors
1973   Named a "Washingtonian of the Year" by
        Washingtonian Magazine
1980   "Community Service Award," by American Society of
        Civil Engineers - National Capitol Section
1982   "Tom Bradley Leadership Award," by National
        Association of Regional Councils
1984   Professional Achievement in Engineering Award, by
        Iowa State University
1987   AASHTO President's Special Award of Merit, "In
        recognition and appreciation of his outstanding efforts
        on behalf of the state highway and transportation
        departments to secure enactment of the Surface
        Transportation and Uniform Relocation Assistance Act
        of 1987, and to expand the international awareness and
        participation of AASHTO"
1989   W.N. Carey, Jr. Distinguished Service Award "In
        Recognition of Outstanding Administrative Leadership
        and Support of Research Activities," by the
        Transportation Research Board, the National Research
        Council and the National Academy of Sciences
1990   P.D. McLean Memorial Award "For Outstanding
        Contributions to the Advancement of Highway
        Transportation in the Public Interest," by The Road
        Gang
1993   Theodore M. Matson Memorial Award, by Institute of
        Transportation   Engineers, Highway Users
        Federation, American Road and Transportation
        Builders Association, Federal Highway Administration
        and AASHTO
1995   Named to Chi Epsilon National Civil Engineering
        Honor Society, by Iowa State University Chapter of
        ASCE
1997   George S. Bartlett Award "For making an outstanding
        contribution to highway progress", by Transportation
        Research Board, American Road and Transportation
        Builders Association, and AASHTO

1999   President's Award for Lifetime Achievement, by
        Intelligent Transportation Society of America
1999   Silver Hardhat Award for Service to the Industry, by
        Construction Writers Association
2000   Establishment of continuing *Francis B. Francois Award
        for Innovation* by the American Association of State
        Highway and Transportation Officials (AASHTO), to
        be bestowed annually upon a state department of
        transportation that has developed innovative
        transportation projects, and including a $10,000
        graduate fellowship from AASHTO to be conferred
        upon an applicant pursuing an advanced
        transportation related degree at a state university
        designated by that department of transportation.
2002   Named Honorary Life Member of the Institute of
        Transportation Engineers
2003   Received Marston Medal from Iowa State University,
        its highest engineering award for engineering alumni.
2004   Named one of America's top 100 private sector
        transportation design and construction professionals of
        the 20th century.
2007   Received Turner Medal from Transportation Research
        Board in recognition of Lifetime Achievement in
        Transportation

Selected Publications and Presentations
    (Excluding Congressional Testimony presented on behalf of the
National Association of Counties, the National Association of Regional
Councils and the American Association of State Highway and
Transportation Officials (AASHTO), and AASHTO Work Products)

    "The Buying of the Pentagon, or What Are the PIGS All About?"
June, 1971 issue, *"THE AMERICAN COUNTY,"* National Association
of Counties, Washington, D.C.

    "Who Will Make Our Regional Decisions?," November, 1972
issue of *" NATION'S CITIES"* magazine, National League of Cities,
Washington, D.C.

    "Working with Policy Officials," Chapter 4, *"REGIONAL
COUNCIL COMMUNICATIONS,"* National Assoc. of Regional
Councils, Washington, D.C. 1973

"Urban Water Resources - The Politics of Management,"
"ENGINEERING ISSUES," American Society of Civil Engineers, New
York, New York, July, 1973

"The Dilemma of Regionalism for Local Officials," January, 1974
issue *"PUBLIC MANAGEMENT"*, International City Management
Association, Washington, D.C.

"Putting the Costs 'Up Front," Volume I, *"MANAGEMENT AND
CONTROL OF GROWTH,"* The Urban Land Institute, Washington,
D.C., 1975

"Association Housing and Local Government," "SUMMARY OF
PROCEEDINGS," Community Associations Institute, Washington,
D.C., 1975

"208 - A Report: The View from Local Government," September,
1976 issue of *"PRACTICING PLANNER"* magazine, American Institute
of Planners, Washington D.C.

"Counties and Intergovernmental Relationships Facing the Third
Century," prepared for the *Symposium on the Future of County
Governments,* Boston, MA, September, 1976

"Enhanced Role for Counties Seen in Scientific Research," April
17, 1978 issue of *"COUNTY NEWS,"* National Association of Counties

"Keynote Address," *Proceedings of the 33rd Virginia Highway and
Transportation Conference,* Virginia Military Institute, Lexington, VA,
November 17-18, 1983

"Needed: A New Consensus in Congress," February, 1985 issue
of *"CONCRETE PIPE NEWS,"* American Concrete Pipe Association

"Keynote Address," *Workshop Presentations Including Ideas that
Work,* International Bridge, Tunnel and Turnpike Association, New
Orleans, LA, April 14-16, 1985

"Maintenance is Forever," keynote address, Pan American
Highway Maintenance Conference, Los Angeles, CA, September 10,
1985

"Engineering, Operations and Highway Safety - An AASHTO Perspective," presentation to Safety Conference for State Highway Operations and Traffic Law Enforcement Officials, Hershey, PA, March, 1988

"AASHTO and the Highway Agencies of the United States - is the U.S. Experience of Value for France?," presentation at PIARC, Paris, France, April, 1988

"A Look Ahead," presentation to American Society of Highway Engineers annual meeting, Harrisburg, PA, May 13, 1988

"The Next Century - Keeping America Moving," May, 1989 issue, " CONSTRUCTOR MAGAZINE"

"We Must Keep America Moving," keynote address, National Transportation Public Affairs Workshop, Oklahoma City, OK, August, 1989

"Transportation Data - Getting More But Avoiding Information Gridlock," presentation to Transportation Research Board Conference on "Transportation Data and Information Systems, Washington, D.C., October 24, 1989

"Hot Mix Asphalt in Practice in the U.S.," presentation to first International Conference on the Best Construction Practices for HMA Pavement, Kauai, HI, January, 1990

"Highways and Transit - What Does the Future Hold?" presentation to National League of Cities committee, Washington, D.C., February 13, 1992

"Implementing the Intermodal Surface Transportation Efficiency Act," June, 1992 issue, "CONSTRUCTOR MAGAZINE"

"Federal-aid Highway System: A State Perspective," PIARC's "ROADS/ROUTES" magazine, Paris, France, 1992

"Financing Highways and Bridges in the United States," prepared for Transportation Association of Canada's workshop, "Financing Canada's Multi-Modal Infrastructure," Quebec, Canada, September 16, 1992

"Perspectives on the ISTEA Vision - Progress and Issues," presentation to ITE International Conference, Orlando, FL, March 15, 1993

"Plans and Priorities for Implementation of SHRP Products," presentation to Pacific Rim TransTech Conference, Seattle, WA, July 28, 1993

"Who Are the Customers?," presentation to Thirtieth Kentucky Forum on Transportation, Lexington., KY, September 16, 1993

"State Roles in Transit Since ISTEA," presentation to FTA/AASHTO State Programs Conference, Washington, D.C., July 25, 1994

"Setting Public Agency Telematics Priorities and a Look at Public Agency Telematic Responsibilities," presentation to First ITS World Congress, November, 1994, Paris, France

"State Perspective," presentation to TRB Conference on Institutional Aspects of Metropolitan Transportation Planning, Williamsburg, VA, May 21, 1995

"The New England Transportation Consortium," with co-author Thomas Humphrey, July-August, 1995 issue of *"TR NEWS,"* Transportation Research Board

"NQI'S Widening Circle of Quality," presentation to National Quality Initiative conference, Washington, D.C., November, 1995

"Highway Finance - Entering the Second Century," Semisequicentennial Transportation Conference, Ames, IA, May 13-14, 1996

"Future Funding Needs," September-October, 1998 issue of *"TR NEWS,"* Transportation Research Board

"Some Goals Achieved - New Challenges to Meet," November-December, 1998 issue of *"TR NEWS,"* Transportation Research Board

"Interview," published in Spring, 1999 issue of *"TRANSPORTATION QUARTERLY,"* Eno Transportation Foundation, Inc.

"Transportation -Then, Now and Tomorrow," Chairwoman's Luncheon address at 1999 TRB meeting, January 13, 1999 - published in July, 1999 *issue of "PUBLIC WORKS MANAGEMENT AND POLICY,"* Sage Publications, Inc.

"Chapter 1, Introduction," *Intelligent Transportation Primer* textbook, copyright 2000, by the Institute of Transportation Engineers, ISBN 0-935403-45-0

"21st Century Linkage Between Transportation and the Economy," paper prepared for TRB Conference on Transportation and Economic Development, Portland, OR, September 23-25, 2001 - postponed to May, 2002, after September 11, 2001 incident

"Overview - Transportation as a Strategy for a Better Quality of Life," paper prepared for presentation to the 17th Annual Fall Planning Conference of the Illinois DOT, October 25&26, 2001, at Starved Rock Lodge, Utica, Illinois

"Why We Need To Preserve the Professions Memory," paper prepared for 2002 Transportation Research Board meeting, Session 241

Personal

Born January 21, 1934 on a farm near Barnum, Iowa. Attended grades 1-12 at the Johnson Township Consolidated School in Barnum, and graduated from high school in 1952. Engaged in farming near Barnum on land held in the family for over 100 years. Married February 6, 1960 in Maryland to Eileen Mary Schmelzer; five children, Joseph Francis, Marie Eileen, Michael David, Monica Irene and Susan Rose, and seven grandchildren: Brendan, Conor and Alison (Joseph), Eileen, Elizabeth and Julia (Marie), Ash (Monica).

# # #

Marston Medal

Turner Medal

Autobiography of Eileen Schmelzer

These next few pages contain the Autobiography of Eileen Schmelzer, written upon graduating High School. The complete text is included after the images of the pages.

DEDICATED

to

The Holy Family

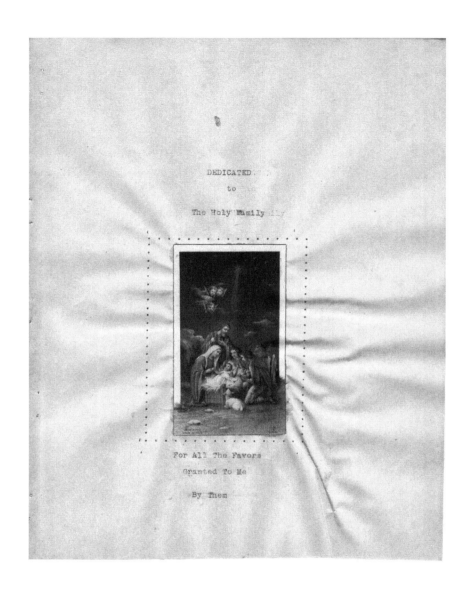

For All The Favors

Granted To Me

By Them

MY AUTOBIOGRAPHY

by

Eileen Schmelzer

TABLE OF CONTENTS

Chapter   Page

I...Family Background.....................1

II..Early Childhood.......................4

III.Upper Grade School Days...............6

IV..High School Days.............. 9

V...My Character..... 11

1.

CHAPTER I

FAMILY BACKGROUND

Although Greenoch, Scotland, and Allentown, Pennsylvania, are thousands of miles apart, my parents bridged them very nicely when they met.

In the little town of Greenoch, Scotland, Eileen Woods was born. Shortly after her birth, her father died, and Mrs. Woods took the children with her to their grandfather's. He had traveled all over the world, as a ship's carpenter and cabinet-maker, and it was from him that Eileen acquired her vast knowledge of the various woods used in furniture and cabinet-making.

One of Eileen's earliest memories is of going down to the docks with her grandfather when the various ships came in. He was never very interested in the passenger ships, but he took Eileen on practically all the cargo ships that docked in Liverpool. Eileen has often said that she learned more geography during those trips than she ever did in later years.

During one of his journeys around the world, her grandfather purchased a hammered gold and silver shawl which now belongs to Eileen, and she cherishes it as a remembrance of him. It was her grandfather that she missed most of all when her mother brought her and her two sisters to this country.

About eight years prior to Eileen Woods arrival in the states,

150

Mr. & Mrs. Anthony Schmelzer had moved from Allentown, Pennsylvania, wher their youngest son, Ludy, had been born, to New York, where
they established themselves in the catering business. Ludy's favorite ambition was to travel extensively, but his age, pocket book,
and school requirements didn't contribute much toward his doing
this; therefore he used to ride the New York Elevated from one end
of the city to the other when he had some free time. He also loved
to read, and he would take a book along and read it during his travels on the Elevated.

It was about four years afte r
Eileenes arrival in New York that her
mother & the Schmelzers became business neighbors. They operated establishments next door to each other
for a number of years, and it was during that time that Eileen and Ludy
met. Eileen was sixteen, and allowed
out only occasionaly, and then to
group activities. However, Ludy was
always one of the group, and by the
time Eileen was eighteen they were going steadily with each other, with the
understanding of marriage in the near
future.

"they were going together"

When Ludy was twenty-six, and Eileen twenty, they were married,
and went to Bermuda on their honey-moon. Right after their marriage came the financial crash of 1929. Fortunately they had both been

raised to find enjoument within the home, for during the depression years their only pastimes were early Sunday morning concerts at Radio City Music Hall, and evenings of bridge with their friends.

These first years of their marriage were hard years in every way, but they were happy ones too, as the bright hope of having a family was always there. However, it was almost seven years before they were so blessed.

"on their honeymoon"

CHAPTER II

EARLY CHILDHOOD

As the snow fell softly on the night of December 1, 1934, there was heard in Bethany Deaconess Hospital, Glendale, N.Y. the cry of a new born baby. About ten days after my birth, I was baptized Eileen Schmelzer. For the first six month's of my life I lived in Queen's County, and then, with my parents I moved to the Mountain

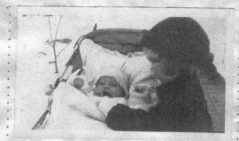

Lake Country Club, where my father was manager.

While we were living at the club, my brother, James, was born on October 6, 1936. One of my favorite pastimes at the age of three was taking my baby brother out in

"pushing my baby brother in his carriage"

the afternoon in his carriage. I think that both my brother and I acquired our love of the out-of-doors from living in the mountains when we were very young.

When James was a year oud, Dad and Mother decided to move to Flushing, N. Y., where we lived until I was about six years old.

One of my best memories of this time is of a party given by the
little boy next door when I was bout four years old. The boy's
grandfather had been sent to the dimestore for some favors suitable for children ranging in age from three to six years o fage.
He returned with water pistols and commenced to fill them for us;
as a result, the party turned into a water battle. Nevertheless,
I must admit, we had a good time even if we were soaking wet.

After living in Flushing, we moved to Miami, Florida, for a
short stay, and from there we moved to Washington, D. C.. I began the third grade at Blessed Sacrament School in Chevy Chase.

It was here at Blessed Sacrament that I prepared for my first
Holy Communion. I can still the
remember the day that I received
the Holy Eucharist for the first
time, and I'm sure it will remain
in my mind as the happiest day of
life.

During the summer that I was
eight, we moved to Hyattsville Md.,

"party when I was four"

and I then entered the fourth grade
at St. James, Mt. Rainier. I hope you'll read the next chapter,
for in it I tell the story of the grade school days of the little
baby born in Bethany Deaconess Hospital, N. Y.

CHAPTER III

UPPER GRADE SCHOOL DAYS

They were strange, those first few weeks at St. James, but
I soon became as much a part of the school as anyone else. I
don't remember too much about my first two years at St. James, but
I do know that I made quite a few friends there that are still very
close friends now: one of these is Jeannine Gadwa, one of classmates
even now.

During the seventh grade, tow things happened that I will always remember, although they are not related to one another in any
way. The first was the day I made my Confirmation. I can still
remember choosing Mary as my confirmation name, and the blow on the
cheek from the bishop. The other was a party given by the coach of
the boys' base-ball team. Several girls from   girls from the
seventh grade   were invited by
the coach, and   we all had a good
time, even the   boys, although they
insisted they   couldn't stand girls
and didn't see   way we were invited.
It was the   summer between the
seventh and   eighth grades that
my family and I   spent at a beach near
Annapolis. The   most enjoyable day of

"My Confirmation"

of that vacation was the day we went to the Naval Academy at Annapolis. We all spent a whole day there, and we even inspected several of the huge ships in the Harbor.

Soon after the Christmas vacation, when we were honorable eight graders, the girls were picked for May Queen, and Purity. I had the honor of being chosen as one of Purity's court. We wore long white organdy dresses that had been made by our mothers, and carried lilies. I never realized that I was going to be sorry that I was leaving grade school but during the last two weeks of school I began to think of all

" the family at Annapolis"

the good times at St. James, and how I would miss my classmates. The day of Graduation arrived; we went to Mass in the morning, the girls in their white dresses, and the boys in their blue shirts. After Mass we had our class picture taken and then we went home. We were going to have a party in the evening, but for now we had nothing to do but go home and remember.

That evening we again appeared at St. James, this time in our best "Bib and Tucker." Several of us girls were in a little skit called "April Showers," and we also sang our version of "Now is the Hour." After the entertainment we had the class prophecies, and then we all just fooled around and had a wonderful time. Although we were all glad that we were old enough to graduate, we were sad at the idea of leaving the school where we had made so many fiends, and spent so many years.

High school was a wonderful word, but we had heard so much about the way Freshmen were treated that we were quite anxious about starting high school. I had chosen Immaculate Conception Academy as my home stead for the next four years, and I was looking forward to the opening day of school.

CHAPTER IV

MY HIGH SCHOOL DAYS

As well as I can remember, the first few days of high school
I went around in a fog. Every thing was so new, and I soon found
out that my friends had been right when they said, "There is nothing so low and worthless as a freshman."

Just a few days after school began we met our big "Sister".
These "big sisters" were seniors who were supposed to help us get
settled in Immaculate. Inpayment for their aid, they asked very
little; we were expected to do nothing for them except obey their
commands, and every other word we heard was a command. Despite
the teasing we had to put up with, there were many beautiful ceremonies attached to entering Immaculate. Among these was the receiv-
of a red rose from Father Ward, the pastor. This rose was a symbol
of the ideals and standards of Immaculate, and every girl who received
it felt glad that she was to be a part of the wonderful I. C. A. and
all its beautiful traditions.

Every year the Juniors give the Christmas play, and some of the
freshmen are angels. I was very proud when sister chose me to be one
of the angels. In May of my freshman the whole school went to Emmitsburg for the Marynoll Congress. We all had a very interesting time,
listening to the lectures and debates. The priests at Mount St. Mary's
had given us permission to eat lunch near their lovely shrine of

the Blessed Virgin, and we did so, saying a rosary while we were there.

The sophomore year was a little harder than the freshman, but I managed to get through it without too many mishaps.

The junior year, upper classmen,----these were the phrases that ran through my mind the first day of my junior year. No longer would the upper classman look at me as if they wondered what I was, because I was now one of them.

During the summer I began to pay more attention to boys, parties and the like. I guess this is all just a part of growing up. I also began to take more of an interest in sports,among them golf, baseball, and roller skating.

During the last three years I have made many friends, among them the boys and girls that I spend most of my leisure time with. My first three years at Immaculate have been good ones, and if my last is anything like them I shall be very content.

"The summer of my sophomore year"

CHAPTER V

MY CHARACTER

It has been said that we should look into our selves first, and then into the characters of others. This is what I intedn to do. I, like everyone else, have my good and bad points.

I fell that among my bad points my habit of talking too loud and two fast stands out as about the worst, but I think that I am beginning to control this habit. It is also my opinion that I take offense too easily at what others say to me, I realize that they correct me for my own good, but I usually forget this.

As I am human I must have some good points, and I feel that my most prominent one is the fact that I get along well with others. I make friends easily, and I rarely lose one.

Although I help around the house, I have the habit of being disagreable when I am asked to do something. I think that this shows that I am selfish, but I do try to overcome this trait. I like to help others, although I often forget that "charity begins at home." In my opinion I am cutting down my bad points, although I still have quite a way to go yet,

My Autobiography
By Eileen Schmelzer

Dedicated to The Holy Family
For All the Favors Granted to Me By Them

CHAPTER 1
FAMILY BACKGROUND

Although Greenoch, Scotland, and Allentown, Pennsylvania are thousands of miles apart, my parents bridged them very nicely when they met.

In the little town of Greenoch, Scotland, Eileen Woods was born. Shortly after her birth, her father died, and Mrs. Woods took the children with her to their grandfather's. He had traveled all over the world, as a ship's carpenter and cabinet-maker, and it was from him that Eileen acquired her vast knowledge of various woods used in furniture and cabinet-making.

One of Eileen's earliest memories is of going down to the docks with her grandfather when the various ships came in. He was never very interested in the passenger ships, but he took Eileen on practically all the cargo ships that docked in Liverpool. Eileen has often said that she learned more geography during those trips than she ever did in later years.

During one of his journeys around the world, her grandfather purchased a hammered gold and silver shawl which now belongs to Eileen, and she cherishes it as a remembrance of his. It was her grandfather that she missed most of all when her mother brought her and her two sisters to this country.

About eight years prior to Eileen Woods arrival in the states, Mrs. & Mrs. Anthony Schmelzer had moved from Allentown, Pennsylvania, where their youngest son, Ludy, had been born, to New York, where they established themselves in the catering business. Ludy's favorite ambition was to travel extensively, but his age, pocket book, and school requirements didn't contribute much toward his doing this; therefore he used to ride the New York Elevated from one end of the city to the other when he had some free time. He also loved to read, and he would take a book along and read it during his travels on the Elevated.

It was about four years after Eileen's arrival in New York that her mother and the Schmelzers became business neighbors. They operated establishments next door to each other for a number of years, and it was during that time that Eileen and Ludy met. Eileen was sixteen, and allowed out only occasionally, and then to group activities. However, Ludy was always one of the group, and by the time Eileen was eighteen they were going steadily with each other, with the understanding of marriage in their near future.

When Ludy was twenty-six, and Eileen twenty, they were married, and went to Bermuda on their honey-moon. Right after their marriage came the financial crash of 1929. Fortunately they had both been raised to find enjoyment within the home, for during the depression years their only pastimes were early Sunday morning concerts at Radio City Music Hall, and evenings of bridge with their friends.

These first years of their marriage were hard years in every way, but they were happy ones too, as the bright hope of having a family was always there. However, it was almost seven years before they were so blessed.

CHAPTER II
EARLY CHILDHOOD

As the snow fell softly on the night of December 1, 1934, there was heard in Bethany Deaconess Hospital, Glendale, N.Y. the cry of a new born baby. About ten days after my birth, I was baptized Eileen Schmelzer. For the first six months of my life I lived in Queen's County, and then, with my parents I moved to the Mountain Lake Country Club, where my father was manager.

While we were living at the club, my brother, James, was born on October 6, 1936. One of my favorite pastimes at the age of three was taking my baby brother out in the afternoon in his carriage. I think that both my brother and I acquired our love of the out-of-doors from living in the mountains when we were very young.

When James was a year old, Dad and Mother decided to move to Flushing, N.Y., where we lived until I was about six years old. One of my best memories of this time is of a party given by the little boy next door when I was bout four years old. The boy's grandfather had been sent to the dimestore for some favors suitable for children ranging in age from three to six years of age. He returned with water pistols and commenced to fill them for us; as a result, the party turned into a water battle. Nevertheless, I must admit, we had a good time even if we were soaking wet.

After living in Flushing, we moved to Miami, Florida, for a short stay, and from there we moved to Washington, D.C. I began third grade at Blessed Sacrament School in Chevy Chase. It was here at Blessed Sacrament that I prepared for my first Holy Communion. I can still remember the day that I received the Holy Eucharist for the first time, and I'm sure it will remain in my mind as the happiest day of my life.

During the summer that I was eight, we moved to Hyattsville, Maryland, and I then entered the fourth grade at St. James, Mt. Rainier. I hope you'll read the next chapter, for in it I will tell the story of the grade school days of the little baby born in Bethany Deaconness Hospital, N.Y.

CHAPTER III
UPPER GRADE SCHOOL DAYS

They were strange, those first few weeks at St. James, but I soon became as much a part of the school as anyone else. I don't remember too much about my first two years at St. James, but I do know that I made quite a few friends there that are still very close friends now; one of these is Jeannine Gadwa, one of my classmates even now.

During the seventh grade, two things happened that I will always remember; although they are not related to one another in any way. The first was the day I made my Confirmation. I can still remember choosing Mary as my confirmation name, and the blow on the cheek from the bishop. Then there was a party given by the coach of the boy's baseball team. Several girls from the seventh grade were invited by the coach, and we all had a good time, even the boys, although they insisted they couldn't stand girls and didn't see why we were invited.

It was the summer between the seventh and eighth grades that my family and I spent at a beach near Annapolis. The most enjoyable day of that vacation was the day we went to the Naval Academy at Annapolis. We all spent a whole day there, and we even inspected several of the huge ships in the Harbor.

Soon after the Christmas vacation, when we were honorable eight graders, the girls were picked for May Queen, and Purity. I had the honor of being chosen as one of the Purity's court. We wore long white organdy dresses that had been made by our mothers, and carried white lilies.

I never realized that I was going to be sorry that I was leaving grade school but during the last two weeks of school I began to think of all the good times at St. James, and how I would miss my classmates. The day of Graduation arrived; we went to Mass in the morning, the girls in their white dresses, and the boys in their blue shirts. After Mass we had our class picture taken and then we went home. We were going to have a party in the evening, but for now we had nothing to do but go home and remember.

That evening we again appeared at St. James, this time in our best "Bib and Tucker." Several of us girls were in a little skit called "April Showers," and we also sang our version of "Now is the hour." After the entertainment we had the class prophecies, and then we all just fooled around and had a wonderful time. Although we were glad that we were old enough to graduate, we were sad at the idea of leaving the school where we had made so many friends, and spent so many years.

High school was a wonderful word, but we had heard so much about the way Freshmen were treated that we were quit anxious about starting high school. I had chosen Immaculate Conception Academy as my homestead for the next four years, and I was looking forward to the opening day of school.

CHAPTER IV
MY HIGH SCHOOL DAYS

As well as I can remember, the first few days of high school I went around in a fog. Everything was so new, and I soon found out that my friends had been right when they said, "There is nothing so low and worthless as a freshman."

Just a few days after school began we met our big "Sister." These "big sisters" were seniors who were supposed to help us get settled in Immaculate. In payment for their aid, they asked very little; we were expected to do nothing for them except obey their commands, and every other word we heard was a command. Despite the teasing we had to put up with, there were many beautiful ceremonies attached to entering Immaculate. Among these was the receipt of a red rose from the pastor. This rose was a symbol of the ideals and standards of Immaculate, and every girl who received it felt glad that she was to be a part of the wonderful I.C.A. and all its beautiful traditions.

Every year the Juniors gave the Christmas play, and some of the freshmen are angels. I was very proud when sister chose me to be one of the angels. In May of my freshman year, the whole school went to Emmitsburg for the Maryknoll Congress. We all had a very interesting time listening to the lectures and debates. The priests at Mount St. Mary's had given us permission to eat lunch near their lovely shrine of the Blessed Virgin, and we did so, saying a rosary while we were there.

The sophomore year was a little harder than the freshman, but I managed to get through it without too many mishaps.

The junior year, upper classmen, ----these were the phrases that ran through my mind the first day of my junior year. No longer would the upper classmen look at me as if they wondered what I was, because I was now one of them.

During the summer I began to pay more attention to boys, parties and the like. I guess this is all just a part of growing up. I also began to take more of an interest in sports, among them golf, baseball, and roller-skating.

During the last three years I have made many friends, among them the boys and girls that I spend most of my leisure time with. My first three years at Immaculate have been good ones, and if my last is anything like them I shall be very content.

CHAPTER V
MY CHARACTER

It has been said that we should look into our selves first, and then into the characters of others. This is what I intend to do. I, like everyone else, have my good and bad points.

I feel that among my bad points my habit of talking too loud and too fast stands out as about the worst, but I think that I am beginning to control this habit. It is also my opinion that I take offense too easily at what others say to me, I realize that they correct me for my own good, but I usually forget this.

As I am human I must have some good points, and I feel that my most prominent one is the fact that I get along well with others. I make friends easily, and I rarely lose one.

Although I help around the house, I have the habit of being disagreeable when I am asked to do something. I think that this shows I am selfish, but I do try to overcome this habit. I like to help others,

although I often forget that "charity begins at home."
In my opinion I am cutting down my bad points,
although I still have quite a way to go yet.

PRIMARY SCHOOLS
DADE COUNTY, FLORIDA, PUBLIC SCHOOL SYSTEM
JAMES T. WILSON, Superintendent, Miami, Florida

PROGRESS REPORT
Grades 1, 2, 3

Name _Eileen Schmelzer_

Grade _1 B_ Date of Birth _12-1-34_

School _Coral Way Elementary_

Address _1950 S.W. 13 Ave._

Teacher _Mrs. Merle Knox_

To Parents:

A report of your child's progress will be sent to you every six weeks. The first part of this report will show progress in habits and attitudes. This part is placed first because it is the more important. Habits and attitudes which are developing in a normal and satisfactory way will not be checked, while those in need of improvement will be checked thus (V).

Encourage your child to KEEP THE RECORD CLEAN.

The second part of the card will show progress in school subjects. The letters S, and U will indicate satisfactory, and unsatisfactory progress. MORE THAN ONE UNSATISFACTORY GRADE ENDANGERS PROMOTION.

If your child's report shows a check mark (V) opposite a habit or an attitude, or if any subject is marked U to indicate unsatisfactory progress, have a conference with the teacher at once, preferably at the school, between 3:00 and 3:30 P. M.

Visit your school and know your principal and your teachers.

Lorraine Byrnes Principal

"The Home and the School Working Together for the Good of the Child"

You are invited to join our Parent-Teacher Association

ATTENDANCE

	1st Six Weeks	2nd Six Weeks	3rd Six Weeks
Days Present	28	28	22
Days Absent	2		2
Times Tardy	0	0	0
Actual Weight	52	54	54
Normal Weight	56	56	56

Parent's Signature

1st Six Weeks _Ludwig Schmelzer_

2nd Six Weeks _Ludwig Schmelzer_

3rd Six Weeks

Date entered _February 3-1941_

Date withdrew

Finished semester Yes _✓_ No

Assigned to Grade _1A_ for next semester

Teacher's signature _Mrs. Merle Knox._

COOK PRINTING CO., MIAMI—1940-41

PROGRESS IN HABITS AND ATTITUDES

	1st Six Weeks	2nd Six Weeks	3rd Six Weeks
HEALTH HABITS			
1. Sits, stands and walks correctly			
2. Is careful about personal appearance			
3. Observes other good health habits			
WORK HABITS			
1. Shows initiative			
2. Shows ability to concentrate			
3. Works independently			
4. Follows directions promptly			
5. Uses time wisely			
6. Takes pride in written work			
SOCIAL ATTITUDE			
1. Is thoughtful of others			
2. Is dependable			
3. Co-operates with the group			
4. Uses self-control			
5. Respects own and school property			
6. Respects authority			

A check (V) shows need of improvement.
KEEP THE RECORD CLEAN

Teacher's comments:

PROGRESS IN ACHIEVEMENT

	1st Six Weeks	2nd Six Weeks	3rd Six Weeks
ARITHMETIC			
1. Is learning number facts			
2. Reasons well			
ART			
3. Is developing skill in handwork	S	S	S
4. Is learning to appreciate beauty			
WRITING			
5. Writes legibly		S	S
ENGLISH			
6. Expresses ideas well orally	S	S	S
7. Is learning to express ideas well in writing			
MUSIC			
8. Participates in music	S	S	S
9. Is developing a sense of rhythm		S	S
READING			
10. Is interested in reading	S	S	S
11. Reads aloud well			S
12. Grasps thought in reading			
SPELLING			
13. Spells correctly			
SCIENCE			
14. Is learning to observe closely	S	S	S

S—Satisfactory
U—Unsatisfactory

Teacher's comments:

Eileen Schmelzer Francois' Report Card

About the Author

Francis B. Francois began his professional career in the U.S. Patent Office in 1956 as a Patent Examiner after graduating from Iowa State University with a degree in engineering. Shortly after moving to Washington, D.C., Frank began attending law school at The George Washington University. He moved on to become a patent advisor for the Applied Physics Laboratory at Johns Hopkins University in 1959, was admitted to the Maryland bar in 1960, and practiced patent and trademark law with the firm of Bacon and Thomas from 1962–1980.

Frank entered politics in Prince George's County, MD, in 1962, serving as a Judge on the Orphan's Court Judge, as County Commissioner and as County Councilman. He was twice elected President of the National Association of Regional Councils and in 1979–1980 was President of the National Association of Counties. In 1980, Frank became Executive Director of the American Association of State Highway and Transportation Officials (AASHTO) where he remained until his retirement in 1999.

Francois was elected to the National Academy of Engineering in 1999, and in 2002 he was recognized with an honorary life membership in the Institute of Transportation Engineers. In 2007, the Transportation Research Board awarded him the Frank Turner Medal in recognition of his Lifetime Achievement in Transportation. In 2003 Iowa State University presented him with the Marston Medal, its highest award for engineering achievement. In 2004 the American Road and Transportation Builders Association (ARTBA) named him as one of America's top 100 private-sector transportation design and construction professionals of the 20th century. Other honors and awards include the George S. Bartlett Award (1997), presented by AASHTO, ARTBA, and TRB; the Theodore M. Matson Memorial Award (1993); and TRB's W. N. Carey, Jr., Distinguished Service Award (1989).

Made in the USA
Columbia, SC
18 February 2021

33158100R00112